The Headway Readers

President and Publisher
M. Blouke Carus

Executive Vice President
Paul Carus

Education Director
Carl Bereiter

General Manager
James S. Heywood

**Director of Curriculum
Development**
Dale E. Howard

**Coordinator of Editorial
Services**
Juanita Raman

Production Manager
LeRoy Ceresa

Art Director
Todd Sanders

Project Leader
Marilyn F. Cunningham

**Curriculum Development
Associate**
Catherine E. Anderson

**Curriculum Development
Assistant**
Diane M. Sikora

On a Blue Hill

The Headway Program
Level C

Editor
Marianne Carus

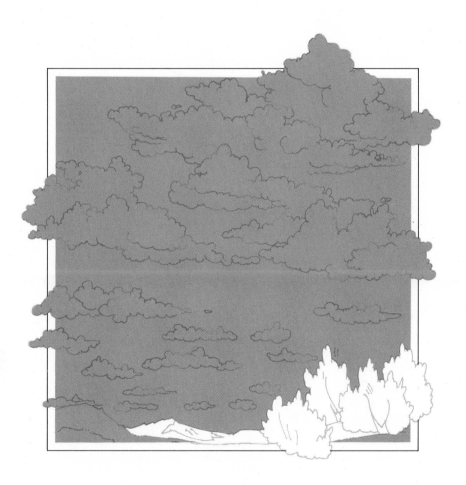

Language Arts Curriculum Development Center

Open Court   La Salle, Illinois

ACKNOWLEDGMENTS:

FOR PERMISSION to reprint copyrighted material, grateful acknowledgment is made to the following publishers and persons:

Addison-Wesley Publishing Company and the Estate of Gertrude Stein for "I Am Rose" from *The World Is Round,* text © 1939, renewed 1967, by Gertrude Stein, a Young Scott Book.

Appleton-Century Crofts Inc. for "The Elf and the Dormouse" by Oliver Herford from *St. Nicholas Magazine;* "Granny and Her Elephant," from *Jataka Tales* by Ellen C. Babbitt, copyright, 1912, by The Century Company. Reprinted by permission of the publisher Appleton-Century, an affiliate of Meredith Press.

Garrard Publishing Co., Champaign, Illinois for "Clouds Tell the Story" by Nancy Larrick, excerpted from *Junior Science Book of Rain, Hail, Sleet and Snow* by Nancy Larrick, copyright 1961 by Nancy Larrick.

Harper and Row, Publishers, Inc. for "Vern" from *Bronzeville Boys and Girls* by Gwendolyn Brooks, copyright 1956, Gwendolyn Brooks Blakely.

Harper and Row, Publishers, Inc. and World's Work Ltd. for "Hill of Fire" adapted from *Hill of Fire* by Thomas P. Lewis, illustrated by Joan Sandin, text copyright © 1971 by Thomas P. Lewis, pictures copyright © 1971 by Joan Sandin; for "The Garden" from *Frog and Toad Together* by Arnold Lobel, copyright © 1971, 1972 by Arnold Lobel; and for "Goblin Story" from *Little Bear's Visit* by Else Holmelund Minarik, illustrated by Maurice Sendak, copyright © 1961 by Else Holmelund Minarik, pictures copyright © 1961 by Maurice Sendak.

George G. Harrap & Company Ltd. for "Little Green Riding Hood" from *Telephone Tales* by Gianni Rodari.

Holt, Rinehart and Winston, Inc. for "Five Little Squirrels," "Me, Myself, and I," and "A Sailor Went to Sea," from *A Rocket In My Pocket,* compiled by Carl Withers, copyright 1948 by Carl Withers.

Holt, Rinehart and Winston, Publishers, and Philip Spitzer for "Do You Ever Wonder?" adapted from *The Ideas of Einstein* by David Fisher, copyright © 1980 by David E. Fisher.

Houghton Mifflin Company for "Why the Magpie's Nest Is Not Well Built," from *The Book of Nature Myths* by Florence Holbrook; "The Little Steam Engine" from the *Riverside Second Reader;* "The Wishing Book" from *The Child's First Book;* and "The Gingerbread Boy" from *Stories for Little Children.*

Gordon Lew for "The Story of the Red Envelopes" from the Chinese Bilingual Program. All rights reserved.

The Macmillan Company for "The Little Turtle" from *Golden Whales of California* by Vachel Lindsay, copyright 1920 by The Macmillan Company, copyright 1948 by Elizabeth C. Lindsay.

G. P. Putnam's Sons for "The Three Billy Goats Gruff," (adapted) from *Popular Tales from the Norse,* by P. C. Asbjörnsen, translated by G. W. Dasent, copyright G. P. Putnam's Sons, 1908.

All possible care has been taken to trace ownership and obtain permission for each selection included. If any errors or omissions have occurred, they will be corrected in subsequent editions, provided they are brought to the publisher's attention.

ISBN 0-89688-450-3

Contents

Part One: Folk Tales Everyone Likes

Part Two: Poems and Fables

Part Three: Stories Old and New

Part Four: For Readers Brave and Bold

Part Five: On Your Own

ILLUSTRATORS:
Ray App (87), Jim Arnosky (33-38, 113, 116), Melanie Arwin (29, 41, 58, 59, 78), Idelette Bordigoni (109, 110, 112), Nan Brooks (83, 139), Joseph Cellini (130, 140, 142), Rick Cooley (22), Barbara Cooney (60, 81), David Cunningham (23, 24, 39, 40, 49), Mike Eagle (118, 120), Hal Frenck (91), Imero Gobatto (53, 55, 137), Michael Hague (72, 89, 146, 147), George Hamblin (94, 95, 97, 173-183), Margaret Hathaway (148, 150), Dennis Hockerman (85), Trina Schart Hyman (57, 102), Arnold Lobel (154-60), Walter Lorraine (74-77), Larry Mikec (16-19, 43-48), Halldor Petursson (124, 125), Barbara Pritzen (122), Joseph Sandin (162-72), Maurice Sendak (3-14), Dan Siculan (107), Jozef Sumichrast (cover), Su Zan Noguchi Swain (31, 99), Lorna Tomei (64-66, 144), Wally Tripp (71), George Ulrich (26, 27, 28, 92), Alessandra Zucchelli (51).

DESIGN:
John Grandits, James Buddenbaum.

Part One

Folk Tales
Everyone Likes

Come, little book, to me;
Come and be my friend.
I'll turn your pages: one, two, three —
Until I reach the end.

Goblin Story

Else Holmelund Minarik

One day a little goblin

went by an old cave.

It was old,

it was cold,

it was dark.

And something inside it went bump.

What was that?

BUMP!

"Hoo-ooh—" cried the goblin.

He got so scared that he jumped
right out of his shoes.
Then he began to run.

Pit - pat - pit - pat - pit - pat —

What was that?

SOMETHING was running after him.

Oh my goodness, what could it be?

The goblin was too scared to look back.

He ran faster than ever.

But so did the SOMETHING that went

pit - pat - pit - pat - pit - pat —

The goblin saw a hole in a tree.

He jumped inside to hide.

The pit - pat - pit - pat came closer,

closer—CLOSER—till it stopped,

right by the hole in the tree!

Then all was quiet.

Nothing happened.

Nothing.

The little goblin wanted to peek out.

It was so quiet.

Should he peek out?

Yes, he would. He WOULD peek out!

And he did.

"Eeeeeh—!" cried the goblin.

Do you know what he saw?

He saw—his SHOES!
His own little shoes
—and nothing more.
"Goodness," said the goblin,
hopping out of the tree.

"That old bump in the cave
made me jump right out of my shoes.
But they came running after me,
didn't they!
And here they are!"

He picked up his shoes,
hugged them,
and put them back on.

"Good little shoes," said the goblin.
"You didn't want to stay behind,
did you!" He laughed.

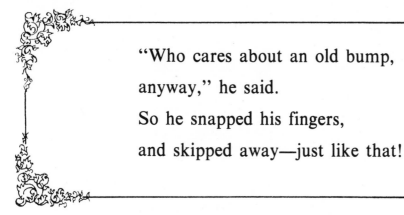

"Who cares about an old bump,
anyway," he said.
So he snapped his fingers,
and skipped away—just like that!

First Names

I. Read and Spell

Ann	Sarah	Barbara
Ruth	Henry	Maureen
Karl	Pedro	Ian
George	Joseph	Catherine
Joan	Ricardo	Kenneth
Maria	Patrick	June

II. Read and Answer

1. What is another name for people with these names?

   Robert   William   Elizabeth   Richard   Thomas

2. What are some other first names? Don't say them if you can't spell them.

The Little Red Hen

English Folk Tale

One day a little red hen found a grain of wheat.

She called the cat.

She called the dog.

She called the pig.

She called the cow.

She said to them,

"Who will help me plant the wheat?"

"Not I," said the cat.

WORDS TO WATCH

wheat   flour   ourselves

16

"Nor I," said the dog.

"Nor I," said the pig.

"Nor I," said the cow.

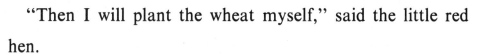

"Then I will plant the wheat myself," said the little red hen.

And she did.

The wheat grew and grew until it was ripe.

"Who will help me cut the wheat?" said the little red hen.

"Not I," said the cat.

"Nor I," said the dog.

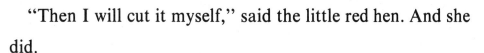

"Nor I," said the pig.

"Nor I," said the cow.

"Then I will cut it myself," said the little red hen. And she did.

When the wheat was all cut, the little red hen said,

"Who will help me take the wheat to the mill?"

"Not I," said the cat.

"Nor I," said the dog.

"Nor I," said the pig.

"Nor I," said the cow.

"Then I will take it myself," said the little red hen. And she did.

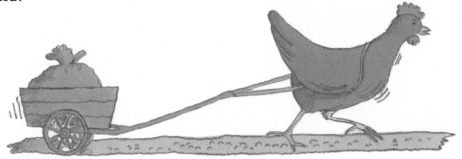

When the wheat was ground into flour at the mill, the little red hen said, "Who will help me bake the bread?"

"Not I," said the cat.

"Nor I," said the dog.

"Nor I," said the pig.

"Nor I," said the cow.

"Then I will bake it myself," said the little red hen. And she did.

When the bread was all baked, the little red hen said,

"Who will help me eat the bread?"

"I will," said the cat.

"I will, too," said the dog.

"I will, too," said the pig.

"I will, too," said the cow.

"No," said the little red hen. "You would not help me plant the wheat or cut the wheat or take it to the mill. And you would not help me bake the bread. My baby chicks and I will eat it all ourselves."

And they did.

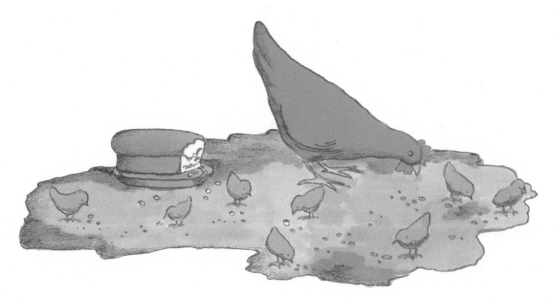

A Great Splish Splash

American Folk Rhyme

If all the seas were one sea,

What a great sea that would be!

And if all the trees were one tree,

What a great tree that would be!

And if all the axes were one ax,

What a great ax that would be!

And if all the men were one man,

What a great man he would be!

And if the great man took the great ax,

And cut down the great tree,

And let it fall into the great sea,

What a splish splash that would be!

Beth Learns to Write

Arther S. Trace, Jr.

David is six years old. He is in the first grade. He likes school. David has a little sister. Her name is Beth. Beth wants very much to go to school. But she is too young. She is only four years old.

WORDS TO WATCH

school	arithmetic	enough
four	bigger	thought
brother	learn	tomorrow

One day Beth said to her brother, "David, what do you do in school?"

"Oh, we read and write and spell," said David, "and we do arithmetic."

"I want to read and write and spell and do arithmetic, too," said Beth.

"You cannot do those things yet," said David. "You are much too little. When you are much bigger, like me, then you can learn all the things that I know."

"I can learn now. I am big enough now. Show me how to read and write now," said Beth.

"Silly," said David. "You are much too little. Wait two more years. Then you can learn."

"No. I want to learn now," said Beth. "Show me how you write your name and then I will write my name."

David thought this was very funny, but he did what his sister asked him to do. He got a pencil and some paper and he wrote:

David

"Now I will write my name," said Beth. Beth took the pencil and wrote:

"There," said Beth, "that is my name."

"No, Beth," said David. "That is not your name. That is my name."

"Then show me how to write my name," said Beth. David smiled. He took the pencil and wrote:

"That is how your name looks," said David. "Do you think you can write it now?"

"Yes, I can write it now," said Beth.

So Beth took the pencil and wrote:

"There," said Beth. "I did write my name. Now I can read and write too. I can read and write better than you can. Tomorrow I will start going to school."

Rhyming Words (with the vowel a)

I. Read and Spell

bat	*make*	*day*	*mail*	*bear*
cat	rake	hay	tail	hair
fat	cake	say	sail	tear
hat	lake	pay	hail	care
mat	bake	gay	pail	fare
rat	take	way	nail	rare

II. Read and Answer

1. Find three words that rhyme with each of these words:

    man   map   game   paw

2. Add more words to the lists in Part I.

III. Write

The fat cat sat with his tail in the pail.

The House That Jack Built

Mother Goose

This is

the house

that

Jack built.

This is the malt

That lay in the house that Jack built.

This is the rat,

That ate the malt

That lay in the house that Jack built.

This is the cat,

That killed the rat,

That ate the malt

That lay in the house that Jack built.

WORDS TO WATCH

built	crumpled	forlorn
worried	maiden	tattered

This is the dog,

That worried the cat,

That killed the rat,

That ate the malt

That lay in the house that Jack built.

This is the cow with the crumpled horn,

That tossed the dog,

That worried the cat,

That killed the rat,

That ate the malt

That lay in the house that Jack built.

This is the maiden all forlorn,

That milked the cow with the crumpled horn,

That tossed the dog,

That worried the cat,

That killed the rat,

That ate the malt

That lay in the house that Jack built.

This is the man all tattered and torn,

That kissed the maiden all forlorn,

That milked the cow with the crumpled horn,

That tossed the dog,

That worried the cat,

That killed the rat,

That ate the malt

That lay in the house that Jack built.

The Story of the Red Envelopes

Gordon Lew

Chinese New Year is here!

May and Ming get up early. They go to greet their grandparents on New Year's Day. Their grandparents give them some red envelopes.

Ming is very happy. He yells: "Oh boy! Money!" Ming opens the first envelope, takes out the money, and throws away the red envelope!

May says, "Ming, don't throw the red envelope away. You're supposed to keep it."

"Why?" asks Ming.

"Because along with the money is a wish from our grandparents. Look! There's something printed on the envelope."

The one Ming had thrown away has a bat on it. The bat means "blessing." The Chinese words bat 蝠 and blessing 福 both sound and look alike. May says, "Look! You've broken the bat's wing!"

Another envelope has a fish on it. It is a wish that in the coming year there will be plenty of food for everyone. The words fish 魚 and plentiful 餘 have the same sound, "yue."

Still another envelope has peaches on it. It is a wish for long life. The Chinese use the peach as a birthday fruit.

Some of the envelopes have old Chinese coins printed on them. These are wishes for a prosperous year. Some have the Chinese words 大 吉 on them, to wish a New Year full of good news and good thoughts. Some have bamboo on them. It is a wish for peace.

Ming says to May, "Wow! There are so many good wishes printed on these red envelopes. I guess I will save the envelopes as well as my money. Thanks for letting me know."

The Little Turtle

Vachel Lindsay

There was a little turtle.

He lived in a box.

He swam in a puddle.

He climbed on the rocks.

He snapped at a mosquito.

He snapped at a flea.

He snapped at a minnow,

And he snapped at me.

He caught the mosquito.

He caught the flea.

He caught the minnow.

But he didn't catch me.

Rhyming Words (with the vowel e)

I. Read and Spell

pet	*seed*	*sheep*	*tea*	*head*
bet	lead	heap	me	shed
let	bead	deep	sea	red
set	need	leap	bee	Ned
wet	read	reap	he	Ted
net	speed	keep	tree	bed

II. Read and Answer

1. Add more words to the lists in Part I.
2. Find and spell three words that rhyme with these words:

seat   beef   end   best

III. Write

1. The bee in the tree will not see me.
2. Ned saw Ted's red head under the bed.
3. The sheep tried to leap and fell in a deep heap.

The Old Woman and Her Pig

English Folk Tale

An old woman went to market and bought a pig.

Pig had four legs,

But pig would not go.

"Well," said the old woman, "what shall I do?"

She went a little farther, and she called to a dog,

"Dog, dog, bite pig.

Pig will not go,

And I should have been home two hours ago."

But the dog would not.

She went a little farther, and she called to a stick,

"Stick, stick, beat dog.

Dog won't bite pig,

Pig will not go,

And I should have been home two hours ago."

But the stick would not.

She went a little farther, and she called to a fire,

"Fire, fire, burn stick.

Stick won't beat dog,

Dog won't bite pig,

Pig will not go,

And I should have been home two hours ago."

But the fire would not.

She went a little farther, and she called to some water,

"Water, water, quench fire.

Fire won't burn stick,

Stick won't beat dog,

Dog won't bite pig,

Pig will not go,

And I should have been home two hours ago."

But the water would not.

She went a little farther, and she called to an ox,

"Ox, ox, drink water.

Water won't quench fire,

Fire won't burn stick,

Stick won't beat dog,

Dog won't bite pig,

Pig will not go,

And I should have been home two hours ago."

But the ox would not.

She went a little farther, and she called to a butcher,

"Butcher, butcher, kill ox.

Ox won't drink water,

Water won't quench fire,

Fire won't burn stick,

Stick won't beat dog,

Dog won't bite pig,

Pig will not go,

And I should have been home two hours ago."

   But the butcher would not.

She went a little farther, and she called to a rope,

"Rope, rope, hang butcher.

Butcher won't kill ox,

Ox won't drink water,

Water won't quench fire,

Fire won't burn stick,

Stick won't beat dog,

Dog won't bite pig,

Pig will not go,

And I should have been home two hours ago."

   But the rope would not.

She went a little farther, and she called to a rat,

"Rat, rat, gnaw rope.

Rope won't hang butcher,

Butcher won't kill ox,

Ox won't drink water,

Water won't quench fire,

Fire won't burn stick,

Stick won't beat dog,

Dog won't bite pig,

Pig will not go,

And I should have been home two hours ago."

But the rat would not.

So she went a little farther, and she called to a cat,

"Cat, cat, kill rat.

Rat won't gnaw rope,

Rope won't hang butcher,

Butcher won't kill ox,

Ox won't drink water,

Water won't quench fire,

Fire won't burn stick,

Stick won't beat dog,

Dog won't bite pig,

Pig will not go,

And I should have been home two hours ago."

"I will kill the rat if you will give me a

saucer of milk," said the cat.

"Very well," said the old woman. So she gave

the cat a saucer of milk, and the cat lapped
it all up.

Then the cat began to kill the rat,

The rat began to gnaw the rope,

The rope began to hang the butcher,

The butcher began to kill the ox,

The ox began to drink the water,

The water began to quench the fire,

The fire began to burn the stick,

The stick began to beat the dog,

The dog began to bite the pig,

The pig began to go;

So it's all over, and the old woman's home again now.

The Oak Tree

A large oak tree is growing at the edge of the meadow. If you listen, you might hear a sparrow singing with all the joy in the world. You might hear the wind blowing through its branches. Or, if you listen very carefully, you might hear the buzzing of bees that live in the center of the trunk.

It is springtime and the flat leaves of the oak tree are green. They will stay green all summer. In the fall the leaves will become bright red or yellow. In the winter the leaves will fall,

---

WORDS TO WATCH

edge   germinate   acorns

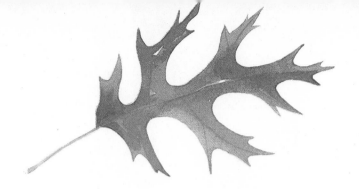

leaving the oak tree bare until the following spring. The new green leaves will grow once again.

Towards the end of summer, acorns will appear and ripen on the branches. Inside each acorn is a seed. Inside each seed is a small new plant. Squirrels and other animals will eat some of the acorns. Other acorns may be carried away by children or washed away during a rainstorm. Sometimes an acorn will remain where it has fallen all winter. Then in the spring, the seed inside it may germinate and grow into a new oak tree. At first it will be small, but after many years it too will become a large oak tree.

This is why people say, "Great oaks from little acorns grow."

QUESTIONS

1. What happens to the leaves of an oak tree during the year?

2. What animals might you find in an oak tree?

3. When someone says, "Great oaks from little acorns grow," what do you think he means?

I Am Rose

Gertrude Stein

I am Rose my eyes are blue

I am Rose and who are you?

I am Rose and when I sing

I am Rose like anything.

Rhyming Words (with the vowel i)

I. Read and Spell

sit	*kite*	*ride*	*mile*
hit	bite	side	pile
bit	bright	tide	tile
fit	light	hide	file
pit	night	wide	dial
lit	tight	lied	style

II. Read and Answer

1. Add more words to the lists in Part I.
2. Find and spell three words that rhyme with each of these words:

    tin   shirt   tire   mice

III. Write

1. It is not right to tie the kite so tight.
2. The bright light might not be right.
3. Curt hurt Bert with some dirt.

The Gingerbread Boy

American Folk Tale

Once upon a time there lived a little old woman and a little old man.

One day the little old woman made a boy out of gingerbread.

She put it into the oven to bake.

By and by she opened the oven door to see if it was done.

Out jumped the Gingerbread Boy!

Away he ran, out of the door and down the road.

The little old woman and the little old man ran after him.

But the Gingerbread Boy looked back and called out,

"Run! run! as fast as you can!

You can't catch me,

I'm the Gingerbread Man, I am! I am!"

And they could not catch him.

The little Gingerbread Boy ran on and on.

Soon he came to a cow.

"Stop, little Gingerbread Boy," said the cow. "I should like to eat you."

But the little Gingerbread Boy called out,

"I've run away from a little old woman,

I've run away from a little old man,

And I can run away from you,

I can! I can!"

The cow ran after him.

But the Gingerbread Boy looked back and called,

"Run! run! as fast as you can!

You can't catch me,

I'm the Gingerbread Man, I am! I am!"

And the cow could not catch him.

The little Gingerbread Boy ran on and on.

Soon he came to a horse.

"Please stop, little Gingerbread Boy," said the horse.

"You look very good to eat."

But the little Gingerbread Boy called out,

"I've run away from a little old woman,

I've run away from a little old man,

I've run away from a cow,

And I can run away from you,

I can! I can!"

The horse ran after him.

But the Gingerbread Boy looked back and called,

    "Run! run! as fast as you can!

    You can't catch me,

    I'm the Gingerbread Man, I am! I am!"

And the horse could not catch him.

By and by the Gingerbread Boy came to a field where a man was working.

The man saw him running and called,

"Do not run so fast, little Gingerbread Boy; you look very good to eat."

But the little Gingerbread Boy ran faster and faster.

As he ran, he called,

    "I've run away from a little old woman,

    I've run away from a little old man,

    I've run away from a cow,

    I've run away from a horse,

    And I can run away from you,

    I can! I can!"

The man in the field ran after him.

But the Gingerbread Boy looked back and called out,

"Run! run! as fast as you can!

You can't catch me,

I'm the Gingerbread Man, I am! I am!"

And the man could not catch him.

Then the little Gingerbread Boy saw a fox.

By this time, the little Gingerbread Boy was very pleased
with himself.

He was pleased that he could run so fast.

So he called out to the fox,

"Run! run! as fast as you can!

You can't catch me,

I'm the Gingerbread Man, I am! I am!

I've run away from a little old woman,

I've run away from a little old man,

I've run away from a cow,

I've run away from a horse,

I've run away from a man in the field,

And I can run away from you, I can! I can!"

"Why," said the fox very politely, "I wouldn't dream of
catching you."

Just then the little Gingerbread Boy came to a river. He

dared not jump into the water. Still, the cow, the horse, and the people were chasing him, and he had to cross the river to keep out of their reach.

"Jump on my tail and I will take you across," said the fox.

So the little Gingerbread Boy jumped on the fox's tail, and the fox swam into the river. A little distance from the shore the fox said,

"Little Gingerbread Boy, I think you had better get on my back or you may fall off!"

So the little Gingerbread Boy jumped on the fox's back.

When they were in the middle of the river, the fox cried out suddenly,

"The water is deep. You may get wet where you are. Jump up on my nose!"

So the little Gingerbread Boy jumped up on the fox's nose.

Then in a twinkling the fox threw back his head and snip, snip, snap! he ate up the Gingerbread Boy!

The Pine Tree

Joan Elma Rahn

Did you ever see a tree with leaves shaped like needles? The pine tree has leaves that look like long, green needles. They do not look like the flat leaves of the oak tree.

The pine tree holds some of its leaves all year around. The tree is always green. It is evergreen.

WORDS TO WATCH		
evergreen	needle	chipmunk
squirrel	piñon	lodgepole

Pine cones grow on the branches of pine trees. In each cone are many seeds. Squirrels and chipmunks eat some of the seeds.

Other seeds fall to the ground. Each seed has a wing. When the seed falls, the wind may blow on the wing. If the wind is strong, it blows the seed away from the tree.

Inside each seed is a small, new plant. After the seed lands on the ground, the little plant in it grows into a new pine tree. It, too, will have cones and needle-shaped leaves.

There are many kinds of pine trees. There are white pines, red pines, pitch pines, lodgepole pines, and others. The seeds of the piñon pine are good to eat.

People use the wood from pine trees to make houses, furniture, boxes, paper, and many other useful things.

QUESTIONS

1. How is a pine tree different from an oak tree?
2. What is inside a pine cone?
3. What is inside a pine seed?
4. What are some kinds of pine trees?
5. What can the wood of pine trees be used for?

Five Little Squirrels

American Folk Rhyme

Five little squirrels sat up in a tree.

The first one said, "What do you see?"

The second one said, "A man with a gun."

The third one said, "Then we'd better run."

The fourth one said, "Let's hide in the shade."

The fifth one said, "I'm not afraid."

Then BANG went the gun, and how they did run.

WORDS TO WATCH

first	third	fifth
second	fourth	squirrels

Numbers (1 to 10)

I. Read and Spell

one	four	eight
two	five	nine
three	six	ten
	seven	

II. Read

three	two	ten
seven	five	eight
four	nine	six
	one	

III. Write

One, two, three, four, five:

I caught a hare alive.

Six, seven, eight, nine, ten:

I let him go again.

The Three Billy Goats Gruff

Norse Folk Tale

Once upon a time there were three billy goats named
Gruff. They were all going up to the hillside to eat the green
grass and make themselves fat.

But on the way up they had to cross a bridge. Under the
bridge lived a great ugly troll, with eyes as big as saucers and
a nose as long as a poker.

WORDS TO WATCH		
troll	youngest	groaned
saucer	tiniest	hoarse
poker	creaked	hardly

The youngest Billy Goat Gruff crossed the bridge first. "Trip, trap! Trip, trap!" went the bridge.

"Who's that tripping over my bridge?" roared the troll.

"Oh! it is only I, the tiniest Billy Goat Gruff. I'm going up to the hillside to make myself fat," said the billy goat with his small voice.

"I'm coming to gobble you up," said the troll.

"Oh, no! Please don't eat me up. I'm too little," said the billy goat. "Wait a bit until the second Billy Goat Gruff comes. He's much bigger."

"Very well. Be off with you, then," said the troll.

A little while later, the second Billy Goat Gruff came across the bridge.

"TRIP, TRAP! TRIP, TRAP! TRIP, TRAP!" went the bridge.

"Who's that tripping over my bridge?" roared the troll.

"It is I, the second Billy Goat Gruff. I'm going up to the hillside to make myself fat," said the second billy goat, who had a louder voice.

"I'm coming to gobble you up," said the troll.

"Oh, no! Don't eat me. Wait a little bit until the big Billy Goat Gruff comes. He's much bigger."

"Very well! Be off with you, then," said the troll.

Just then up came the great big Billy Goat Gruff.

"TRIP, TRAP! TRIP, TRAP! TRIP, TRAP!" went the bridge, for the big billy goat was so heavy that the bridge creaked and groaned under him.

"Who's that tramping over my bridge?" roared the troll.

"IT'S I! THE BIG BILLY GOAT GRUFF," said the billy goat in his big hoarse voice. And he flew at the troll, and poked him and knocked him, and tossed him into the river. After that he went up to the hillside. There the billy goats got so fat that they were hardly able to walk home again. If the fat hasn't fallen off them, they're still fat. And so—

Snip, snap, snout,
This tale's told out.

The Swing

Robert Louis Stevenson

How do you like to go up in a swing,
　　Up in the air so blue?
Oh, I do think it the pleasantest thing
　　Ever a child can do!

Up in the air and over the wall,
　　Till I can see so wide,
Rivers and trees and cattle and all
　　Over the countryside—

Till I look down on the garden green,
Down on the roof so brown—
Up in the air I go flying again,
　　Up in the air and down!

Everyone Has a Job

Anonymous

"I don't feel like going to school today," said María one morning. "I am going for a walk through the fields."

So instead of going to school, María strolled along through the nearby meadow. She walked and walked. The clear blue sky and the fresh air made her feel good. But soon she became bored because there was no one to play with. All her friends were in school.

Suddenly she saw a horse. "Mrs. Horse," said María,

WORDS TO WATCH		
instead	meadow	Mr.
strolled	bored	busy
through	because	nectar

58

"how would you like to run and play with me in the meadow?"

"No, I have no time now to play," said the horse. "I must help my master plow his fields for the spring planting."

So María went on, and before long she met a robin.

"Mr. Robin! Mr. Robin!" María called. "Come and play with me."

"I cannot play with you, little girl," replied the robin. "I am busy finding worms to feed my babies."

María walked on a little farther until she came upon a honeybee.

"Please come and play with me, Miss Bee," said María.

"I cannot play with you," said the bee. "I must gather nectar from the flowers to make honey for food."

Then María began to think. She thought and she thought. Suddenly she ran toward school as fast as she could go.

1. Why didn't María have any children to play with?

2. Whom did María meet in the meadow?

3. What did María learn from talking with the animals in the meadow?

4. Why did María run off to school?

5. Would you have done the same? Why?

The Purple Cow

Gelett Burgess

I never saw a Purple Cow,

    I never hope to see one;

But I can tell you, anyhow,

    I'd rather see than be one.

Rhyming Words (with the vowel o)

I. Read and Spell

hop	*hot*	*floor*	*hook*	*boat*
mop	rot	tore	took	coat
pop	pot	boar	brook	float
top	tot	roar	look	wrote
drop	trot	more	book	goat

II. Read and Answer

1. Add more words to the lists in Part I.
2. Find and spell three words that rhyme with each of these words:

   soup   rope   home   bone

III. Write

1. The cook took the book to the brook.
2. The goat on the boat is eating your coat.
3. Don't drop the pop on top of the mop.

I. A. You have read these stories in your book. Tell what each story is about.

> Goblin Story
>
> The Little Red Hen
>
> The Three Billy Goats Gruff
>
> The Story of the Red Envelopes
>
> Beth Learns to Write
>
> The Old Woman and Her Pig
>
> Everyone Has a Job

B. Which story do you like best? Why?

C. Read the story you like best to your class or read it again to yourself.

II. A. Learn by heart one of the poems you have read in your book and recite it to the class.

B. Copy the poem you like best. Copy it carefully.

Part Two

Poems and
Fables

I've read some stories in my book
I've never read before,
And now that I can read so well
I'm ready for some more.

Old Mother Hubbard

Mother Goose Rhyme

Old Mother Hubbard
Went to the cupboard,
To get her poor dog a bone.
But when she got there
The cupboard was bare,
And so the poor dog had none.

WORDS TO WATCH

cupboard	laughing	fruiterer
joiner	tripe	cobbler
coffin	hatter	delight

She went to the baker's
  To buy him some bread,
But when she came back
  The poor dog was dead.

She went to the joiner's
  To buy him a coffin,
But when she came back
  The poor dog was laughing.

She took a clean dish
  To get him some tripe,
But when she came back
  He was smoking a pipe.

She went to the hatter's
  To buy him a hat,
But when she came back
  He was feeding the cat.

She went to the barber's
  To buy him a wig,
But when she came back
  He was dancing a jig.

She went to the fruiterer's
  To buy him some fruit,
But when she came back
  He was playing the flute.

She went to the tailor's
  To buy him a coat,
But when she came back
  He was riding a goat.

She went to the cobbler's
  To buy him some shoes,
But when she came back
  He was reading the news.

This wonderful dog
  Was Dame Hubbard's delight;
He could sing, he could dance,
  He could read, he could write.

The Tale of a Black Cat

Anonymous

Once there was a little girl named Tamar; and there's a

T that stands for Tamar. Tamar's house was not a very

good one. So she built a new wall on this side of it. ∇ And

then she built a wall on that side of it. ∇ You can see now

that she had two nice rooms in her house, though not very

large. Next she put in windows to look out of—one in this

room ∇ and one in that room. ∇ Then she made a tall

chimney on this side of her house. ∇ And then she made a

tall chimney on the other side of her house. ∇ After that

she started some grass beside her door, like this. ∇

Not far away from Tamar's house lived a little boy named Saul; and there's an $\int$ that stands for Saul. When Tamar had finished her house, she thought she would like to go and tell Saul what she had been doing. So she came out of her door and walked along, this way, over to where he lived. Saul was glad to see her. They went into the kitchen and sat down. Tamar explained to Saul how she had built two new walls to her house and put in windows and made two tall chimneys, and how she had started the grass in front of her door. "And now, Saul," said she, "I want you to come over and see how well I've fixed things."

"I'll put on my cap and go back with you," said Saul. But when he was ready, he said, "We might go down to the cellar first and get some apples to eat on the way." So they went down to the cellar, like this.   They got some apples, and then they came up outdoors by the hatchway, like this.   Now they started for Tamar's house, but the walking was bad. They had gone only a few steps when they tumbled down, like this.

However, they were quickly up, like this.

And they walked along until they were nearly to Tamar's house when they tumbled down again, just like this.

And they were no sooner up on their

feet, like this 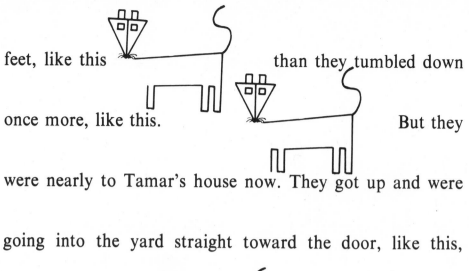 than they tumbled down

once more, like this. But they

were nearly to Tamar's house now. They got up and were

going into the yard straight toward the door, like this,

—when Saul pointed toward the doorstep and cried out,

"O-o-o-o-o-o-hh! See that big BLACK CAT!"

Daddy's Nursery Rhyme

Little Jack Horner
Sat in the corner,
Eating his curds and whey;
　There came a big spider,
　Who sat down beside her,
And the dish ran away with the spoon.

"Daddy, you haven't got it right!"

The Fox and the Grapes

Aesop

One day a fox was running along a dusty road. He was hot and thirsty. Soon he saw some grapes hanging on a vine in a garden nearby.

These grapes were large and ripe and juicy. They looked very good to the fox.

"How I wish I could get some of those grapes," said the fox.

The fox jumped high in the air. But he did not get the grapes.

He jumped again and again. But he still could not get them.

At last he had to give up.

"I am sure they are very sour grapes," said the fox as he walked away. "I do not like sour grapes."

A Sailor Went to Sea

American Folk Rhyme

A sailor went to sea
To see what he could see,
And all that he could see
Was sea, sea, sea.

Little Green Riding Hood

Gianni Rodari

"Once upon a time there was a little girl called Little Yellow Riding Hood."

"No! *Red* Riding Hood!"

"Oh yes, of course, Red Riding Hood. Well, one day her mother called and said: 'Little Green Riding Hood—'"

"Sorry! Red. 'Now, my child, go to Aunt Mary and take her these potatoes.' "

"No! It doesn't go like that! 'Go to Grandma and take her these cakes.' "

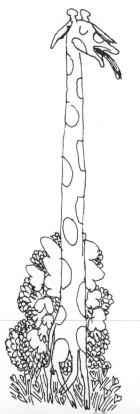

"All right. So the little girl went off and in the wood she met a giraffe."

"What a mess you're making of it! It was a wolf!"

"And the wolf said: 'What's six times eight?' "

"No! No! The wolf asked her where she was going."

"So he did. And Little Black Riding Hood replied—"

"Red! Red!! Red!!!"

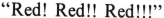

"She replied: 'I'm going to the market to buy some tomatoes.' "

"No, she didn't. She said: 'I'm going to my grandma who is sick, but I've lost my way.' "

"Of course! And the horse said—"

"What horse? It was a wolf."

"So it was. And this is what it said: 'Take the 75 bus, get out at the main square, turn right, and at the first doorway you'll find three steps. Leave the steps where they are, but pick up the dime you'll find lying on them, and buy yourself a packet of chewing gum.' "

"Grandpa, you're terribly bad at telling stories. You get them all wrong. But all the same, I wouldn't mind some chewing gum."

"All right. Here's your dime." And the old man turned back to his newspaper.

The Barnyard

Maud Burnham

When the farmer's day is done,

In the barnyard, every one,

Beast and bird politely say,

"Thank you for my food today."

WORDS TO WATCH		
barnyard	tight	pigeon
politely	animals	neigh
beast	done	sty

78

The cow says, "Moo!"

The pigeon, "Coo!"

The sheep says, "Baa!"

The lamb says, "Maa!"

The hen, "Cluck! Cluck!"

"Quack!" says the duck;

The dog, "Bow Wow!"

The cat, "Meow!"

The horse says, "Neigh!

I love sweet hay!"

The pig near by,

Grunts in his sty.

When the barn is locked up tight,

Then the farmer says, "Good night!"

Thanks her animals every one,

For the work that has been done.

Rhyming Words (with the vowel u)

I. Read and Spell

rug	cut	bump	flute	sound
bug	hut	hump	shoot	wound
tug	nut	lump	root	round
mug	rut	dump	boot	found
dug	jut	stump	fruit	hound
hug	but	jump	hoot	ground

II. Read and Answer

1. Find three words that rhyme with each of these words:

    sun   under   dust   tumble   bull

2. Think of another word with a **u** in it and find words that rhyme with it.

III. Write

A bug dug in the ground and found a nut.

The Hare and the Tortoise

Aesop

One time a hare said to the other animals, "I can beat anybody in a race. I can run like the wind. Who will dare to race with me?"

The animals did not say anything because they were afraid that the hare would beat them.

But then the tortoise said quietly, "I will run a race with you."

"That is a good joke," laughed the hare. "Why, I will be out of sight before you get started."

"Wait until you have won the race before you say anything," said the tortoise. "Shall we race?"

The hare agreed. They chose the starting place and the goal.

The race began, and soon the hare was far ahead of the tortoise.

But the hare ran so fast that he became tired. He stopped by the side of the road and lay down to take a nap. He was sure that he would wake up in time to beat the tortoise.

The tortoise plodded slowly on. When the hare woke up, the tortoise was near the goal.

The hare jumped up and ran as fast as he could toward the goal line, but he was not in time. The tortoise crossed the goal line first and won the race.

The tortoise turned to the other animals and said, "I learned long ago that if you do something steadily you can often do it well, even if you are slow."

QUESTIONS

1. Why did the hare lose the race?
2. Why did the hare laugh when the tortoise said he would race with him?
3. Why were the other animals afraid to race with the hare?
4. Why wasn't the tortoise afraid to race with the hare?
5. What do you think people mean when they say, "Slow and steady wins the race"?

The Rich Man
and the Poor Tailor

Leo Tolstoy

Once upon a time a rich man and a poor tailor lived in the same house. The rich man lived upstairs and the poor tailor lived downstairs.

WORDS TO WATCH
---

once	bothered	became
tailor	richer	finally
upstairs	unhappy	brought
downstairs	because	happier

The tailor liked to sing when she worked. She sang one song after another. But the rich man liked to sleep a lot, and the singing bothered him.

One day the rich man said, "Tailor, I will give you a bag full of money every day if you will stop singing."

"Fine," said the tailor. And so the tailor stopped singing and became richer and richer. But the more money she got from the rich man, the more unhappy she became, because she wanted very much to sing again.

Finally she brought all her money back to the rich man. "Here," she said, "take your money. I cannot be happy if I cannot sing."

And so she gave the money back to the rich man and went away singing. She sang and she sang and she was happier than ever before.

QUESTIONS

1. Why was the tailor happier than ever, after she gave the money back to the rich man?

2. Can you think of other things more important than money?

Cocks Crow in the Morn

Mother Goose

Cocks crow in the morn
   To tell us to rise,
And he who lies late
   Will never be wise;
For early to bed
   And early to rise
Is the way to be healthy,
   And wealthy, and wise.

Clothes

I. Read and Spell

hat	dress	boots	raincoat
cap	shoes	earmuffs	muffler
shirt	scarf	suit	overcoat
socks	tie	rubbers	swimsuit
pants	coat	blouse	sweater

II. Read and Answer

1. Which clothes are worn in snowy weather?
2. Which clothes are worn in all kinds of weather?

III. Write

Boots and coats we wear in snow,

But when the snow and winter go,

Then with its showers comes the spring,

And so our raincoats are the thing.

At last we feel the summer's sun;

Then off go the coats for summer fun.

THE PLUM PIT

Leo Tolstoy

One day a father bought some plums at the store. He took the plums home, put them in a large bowl, and told his children not to eat them until after dinner. All the children stood around the bowl and admired the plums, but they did not eat them.

WORDS TO WATCH

children	know	everyone
worse	admired	laughed

But little Johnny had never tasted plums before. When everyone had left the room, he took one of the plums and ate it.

Before dinner, Johnny's father saw that one of the plums was gone. He told the children's mother about it.

After dinner the children's mother said, "Did any of you children eat one of these plums?"

All the children said, "No." Johnny's face turned red as a beet, but he also said, "No, I didn't eat it."

Then the mother said, "If one of you did eat a plum, that is bad. But that is not what worries me. What is worse is that plums have pits. If you eat the pit, it might choke you, and you might die."

Johnny turned pale and said, "No, I threw the pit out the window."

Then everyone laughed, and Johnny began to cry.

Finally the mother said, "Don't cry, Johnny. We know that you won't do anything like this again."

"No," said Johnny, "I won't. I promise."

1. What did Johnny do?

2. Did he think he was wrong?

3. When Johnny said he threw the pit out the window, why did everyone laugh? Why did Johnny cry?

Little Jack Pumpkin Face

Anonymous

Little Jack Pumpkin Face
   Lived on a vine;
Little Jack Pumpkin Face
   Thought it was fine.

First he was small and green,
   Then big and yellow;
Little Jack Pumpkin Face
   Is a fine fellow.

The Lion and the Mouse

Aesop

One day a mouse by accident ran across the paws of a sleeping lion and woke him up. The lion was very angry at being awakened. He grabbed the mouse and was going to swallow him. But just then the mouse cried out, "Please, kind sir, I didn't mean to wake you up. If you let me go, I can help you some day."

The lion thought that the idea of a mouse helping a lion was so funny that he let the mouse go free.

But only a week later the mouse heard a lion roaring loudly. He went closer to see what the trouble was, and there was the lion caught in a hunter's net. The mouse remembered his promise, and he began to gnaw the rope. He kept gnawing and gnawing until soon the lion was free.

WORDS TO WATCH

mouse	loudly	remembered
accident	closer	promise
awakened	trouble	gnaw
understood		

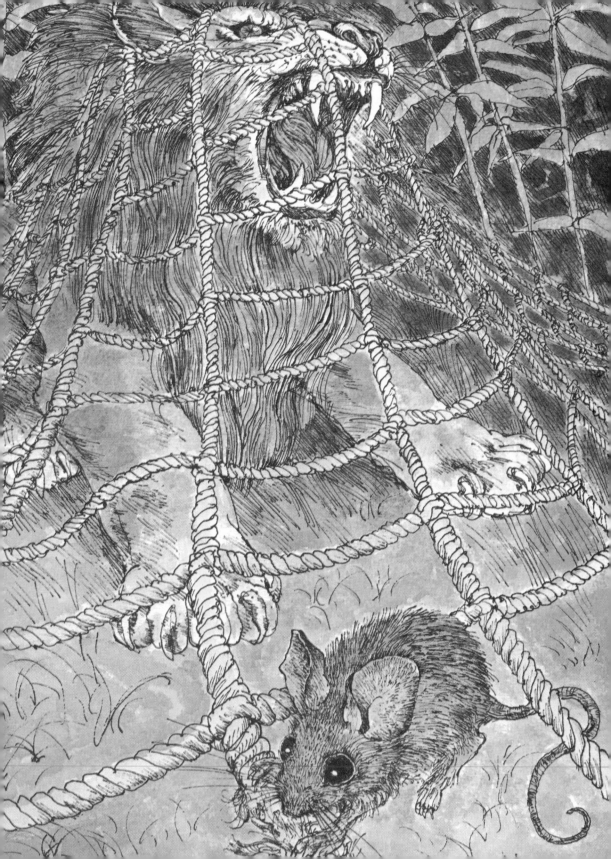

Then the lion understood that little friends can be great friends.

---

1. Why was the lion angry?
2. Why didn't the lion eat the mouse?
3. What did the lion learn?
4. Can you expect kindness to be returned? Why do you feel this way?

Hearts Are Like Doors

Anonymous

Hearts, like doors, will open with ease,

To very, very little keys,

And don't forget that two of these

Are "Thank you" and "If you please!"

92

Colors

I. Read and Spell

red	pink	tan
green	gray	brown
black	white	purple
blue	yellow	orange

II. Read and Answer

1. What colors mixed together make orange?
2. What colors mixed together make green?
3. What colors mixed together make gray?
4. Name some other colors.

III. Write

THE RAINBOW

See those colors way up high?

That's a rainbow in the sky.

Red and yellow and blue and green:

A prettier sight I've never seen.

The Little Engine That Could

Author Unknown

A little steam engine had a long train of cars to pull.

She went along very well till she came to a steep hill. But then, no matter how hard she tried, she could not move the long train of cars.

She pulled and she pulled. She puffed and puffed. She backed and started off again. Choo! Choo!

But no! the cars would not go up the hill.

At last she left the train and started up the track alone. Do you think she had stopped working? No, indeed! She was going for help.

WORDS TO WATCH

engine	sidetrack	scoured
indeed	alongside	merrily

"Surely I can find someone to help me," she thought.

Over the hill and up the track went the little steam engine. Choo, choo! Choo, choo! Choo, choo!

Pretty soon she saw a big steam engine standing on a sidetrack, looking very big and strong. Running alongside, she looked up and said, "Will you help me over the hill with my train of cars? It is so long and heavy that I can't get it over."

The big steam engine looked down at the little steam engine. Then she said, "Don't you see that I have finished my day's work? I have been rubbed and scoured, ready for my next run. No, I cannot help you."

The little steam engine was sorry, but she went on. Choo, choo! Choo, choo! Choo, choo! Choo, choo! Soon she came to a second big steam engine standing on a sidetrack. He was puffing and puffing, as if he were tired.

"He may help me," thought the little steam engine. She ran alongside and asked, "Will you help me bring my train of cars over the hill? It is so long and so heavy that I can't get it over."

The second big steam engine answered, "I have just come in from a long, long run. Don't you see how tired I am? Can't you get some other engine to help you this time?"

"I'll try," said the little steam engine, and off she went. Choo, choo! Choo, choo! Choo, choo!

After a while she came to a little steam engine just like herself. She ran alongside and said, "Will you help me over the hill with my train of cars? It is long and so heavy that I can't get it over."

"Yes, indeed!" said this little steam engine. "I'll be glad to help you, if I can."

So the two little steam engines started back to where the train of cars had been standing. Both little steam engines went to the head of the train, one behind the other.

Puff, puff! Chug, choo! Off they started!

Slowly the cars began to move. Slowly they climbed the steep hill. As they climbed, each little steam engine began to sing, "I—think—I—can! I—think—I—can! I—think—I—can! I—think—I—can! I—think—I—can! I—think—I—can! I—think—I—can! I—think—I—can! I—think—I—can! I—think—I—can!"

And they did! Very soon they were over the hill and going down the other side.

Now they were on the plain again, and the little steam engine could pull her train herself. So she thanked the little engine who had come to help her and said good-bye.

And she went merrily on her way, singing, "I-thought-I-could! I-thought-I-could! I-thought-I-could! I-thought-I-could! I-thought-I-could! I-thought-I-could! I-thought-I-could! I-thought-I-could! I-thought-I-could! I-thought-I-could! I-thought-I-could!"

Betty Botter

Anonymous

Betty Botter bought some butter,
"But," she said, "the butter's bitter;
If I put it in my batter
It will make my batter bitter,
But a bit of better butter
Will make my batter better."
So she bought a bit of butter,
Better than her bitter butter,
And she put it in her batter
And the batter was not bitter.
So 'twas better Betty Botter
  bought a bit of better butter.

Why the Magpie's Nest
Is Not Well Built
American Folk Tale

A long time ago all the birds met together to talk about building nests.

"Every human has a house," said the robin, "and every bird needs a home too."

"Humans have no feathers," said the owl, "and so they are cold without houses. We have feathers."

"I keep warm by flying swiftly," said the swallow.

"And I keep warm by fluttering my wings," said the hummingbird.

"By and by we shall have our little ones," said the robin. "They will have no feathers on their wings, so they cannot fly or flutter, and they will be cold. How shall we keep them warm if we have no nests?"

Then all the birds said, "We will build nests so that our little ones will be warm."

The birds went to work. One brought twigs, one brought moss, and one brought leaves. They sang together merrily, for they thought of the little ones that would sometime come to live in the warm nests.

Now the magpie was lazy. She sat still and watched the others at their work.

"Come and build your nest in the reeds and rushes," cried one bird. But the magpie said, "No."

"My nest is on the branch of a tree," called another, "and it rocks like a child's cradle. Come and build beside it." But the magpie said, "No."

Before long all the birds but the magpie had their nests built. The magpie cried, "I do not know how to build a nest. Will you not help me?"

The other birds were sorry for her and answered, "We will teach you." The blackbird said, "Put the twigs in this bough." The robin said, "Put the leaves between the twigs." And the hummingbird said, "Put this soft green moss over it all."

"I do not know how," cried the magpie.

"We are teaching you," said the other birds. But the magpie was lazy, and she thought, "If I do not learn, they will build a nest for me."

The other birds talked together. "She does not wish to learn," they said, "and we will not help any longer." So they went away from her.

Then the magpie was sorry. "Come back," she cried, "and I will learn." But by this time the other birds had eggs in their nests. They were busy taking care of their eggs and had no time to teach the lazy magpie. This is why the magpie's nest is not well built.

QUESTIONS
---

1. Why didn't the magpie want to build a nest?
2. After the magpie really wanted to build a nest, why didn't the other birds help her?
3. Do you feel sorry for the magpie? Why?

CLOUDS

Christina Rossetti

White sheep, white sheep,
On a blue hill,
When the wind stops
You all stand still.
When the wind blows
You walk away slow.
White sheep, white sheep,
Where do you go?

At Home

I. Read and Spell

rug	kitchen	fireplace
bed	bedroom	radio
lamp	bookcase	living room
porch	closet	T.V. set
stove	armchair	sofa
stairs	garage	attic
yard	telephone	garden
basement	cupboard	pictures

II. Read and Answer

1. Which of these things are not needed in a home?
2. Name some other things in a home.

III. Write

Be it ever so humble, there's no place like home.

I. A. You have read these stories in the second part of your book. Tell what each story is about.

> The Fox and the Grapes
>
> The Plum Pit
>
> The Hare and the Tortoise
>
> Little Green Riding Hood
>
> The Rich Man and the Poor Tailor
>
> Why the Magpie's Nest Is Not Well Built
>
> The Little Engine That Could
>
> The Lion and the Mouse

B. Which story do you like best? Why?

C. Read the story you liked best to your class or read it to yourself again.

II. A. Learn by heart one of the poems in the second part of your book and recite it to your class.

B. Copy the poem you liked best in the second part of your book. Copy it carefully.

Part Three

Stories
Old and New

Of all the stories in my book
I don't know which is best,
But I have liked them all so well
I'm ready for the rest.

VERN

Gwendolyn Brooks

When walking in a tiny rain
Across the vacant lot,
A pup's a good companion—
If a pup you've got.

And when you've had a scold,
And no one loves you very,
And you cannot be merry,
A pup will let you look at him,
And even let you hold
His little wiggly warmness—

And let you snuggle down beside,
Nor mock the tears you have to hide.

The Three Bears

Robert Southey

Once upon a time there were three bears—a great big bear, a middle-sized bear, and a little tiny bear. They all lived together in a house in the middle of a wood.

One day the three bears sat down to breakfast, but their porridge was so hot that they couldn't eat it. They decided to go for a walk in the wood and leave the porridge on the kitchen table to cool off.

While they were away, a little girl named Goldilocks came to the house in the wood. She had been picking flowers since early in the morning and was very tired. When she saw the little house, she said to herself, "Surely the people who live here will let me rest for a while."

She knocked on the door. But nobody came, for the three bears were out walking in the wood. She knocked again, and

---

WORDS TO WATCH

breakfast	early	growled
porridge	knocked	squeaked
Goldilocks	hundred	bounded

still nobody came. Then Goldilocks opened the door and walked right in.

The first things she saw were three bowls of porridge on the kitchen table. Goldilocks was hungry, so she started to eat the great big bowl of porridge.

"This is too hot!" she said to herself.

Then she took a taste from the middle-sized bowl. "This is too cold!" she said to herself.

Then she took a taste from the little tiny bowl. "This is just right!" she said to herself, and she ate it all up.

Then Goldilocks went into the living room to rest for a while, and there she saw three chairs near the fireplace.

First she sat down in the great big chair. "This is too high!" she said to herself.

Then she sat down on the middle-sized chair. "This is too wide!" she said to herself.

Then she sat down in the little tiny chair. "This is just right!" she said to herself, and she sat down so hard that the little tiny chair broke into a hundred pieces.

Then Goldilocks went upstairs, and there she saw three beds standing in a row. First she lay down on the great bed. "This is too hard!" she said to herself.

Then she lay down on the middle-sized bed. "This is too soft!" she said to herself.

Then she lay down on the little tiny bed. "This is just right!" she said to herself, and she fell fast asleep.

After a while the three bears came home from their walk in the wood. They were very hungry now and started to eat their porridge.

The great big bear took one taste from his bowl and growled, "SOMEONE HAS BEEN EATING MY PORRIDGE!"

The middle-sized bear took one taste from her bowl and said, "SOMEONE HAS BEEN EATING MY PORRIDGE!"

The little tiny bear squeaked, *Someone has been eating my porridge and has eaten it all up!*

Then the three bears went into the living room.

"SOMEONE HAS BEEN SITTING IN MY CHAIR!" growled the great big bear.

"SOMEONE HAS BEEN SITTING IN MY CHAIR!" said the middle-sized bear.

"Someone has been sitting in my chair," squeaked the little tiny bear, *"and has broken it all to pieces!"*

Then the three bears went upstairs.

"SOMEONE HAS BEEN SLEEPING IN MY BED!" growled the great big bear.

"SOMEONE HAS BEEN SLEEPING IN MY BED!" said the middle-sized bear.

"Someone has been sleeping in my bed," squeaked the little tiny bear, *"and here she is!"*

His voice woke Goldilocks up. When she saw the three bears, she was so frightened that she jumped out of bed and bounded down the stairs and ran home to her mother as fast as her legs would carry her. And she never went to the house of the three bears again.

QUESTIONS

Do you feel sorry for Goldilocks? Why or why not?

The Wishing Book

Anonymous

Long, long ago in a land far away lived a little girl. She was so little that everybody called her Tiny.

Tiny had no father or mother. She had no home. She went from place to place asking for something to eat.

Sometimes she went to homes where good, kind people lived. They always gave her something.

Sometimes she called at homes where the people were unkind. They would not give her anything; no, not so much as a little piece of bread.

WORDS TO WATCH

---

unkind   clothes   sighed

113

So sometimes Tiny had to go without anything to eat for days.

One night as it was growing dark, Tiny came to a little town. She went from home to home asking for something to eat, but no one would give her a piece of bread.

Poor Tiny walked away into the woods. She sat down under a tree and cried and cried.

"Why do you cry, my child?" asked a little, wee voice.

Tiny looked down. There in the grass was the prettiest little fairy ever seen.

"Who are you?" asked Tiny.

"I am the queen of the fairies. Now tell me why you are crying."

"Oh, fairy queen, I have no father, no mother, no home. Nobody wants me. Tonight no one will give me a piece of bread. One man set a big black dog on me."

"You poor child," said the fairy. "Don't cry. Look at this pretty picture book."

She opened a big book and showed Tiny many pretty pictures. There were pictures of good things to eat, pictures of good clothes, pictures of pretty homes.

"What a pretty book," said Tiny.

"I am glad you like it," said the queen, "for I am going to give it to you."

"Give it to me?" cried Tiny. "Oh, thank you. If I have pretty pictures to look at, I shall forget the unkind people."

"This is a fairy wishing book," said the queen. "Whenever you want anything, just open your book to the picture of the thing you want and say,

'Fairy queen, I call to you,
Make my picture wish come true.' "

Before Tiny could say "Thank you," the fairy flew away.

"Can it be true?" said Tiny. "I will try it right away."

She opened the book to a picture of a bowl of bread and milk and said,

"Fairy queen, I call to you,
Make my picture wish come true."

At once she found in the grass beside her a big bowl of bread and milk.

"This is the best bowl of bread and milk I have ever eaten," she said. "Now I think I will wish for some clothes."

Opening the book to the picture of pretty clothes, she said,

"Fairy queen, I call to you.

Make my picture wish come true."

At once she had new clothes from her hat to her shoes. She began to be happy.

Then she opened her book to the picture of a little home with trees growing all around it. Again she said,

"Fairy queen, I call to you,

Make my picture wish come true."

At once before her was as pretty a little home as only fairies could build.

Tiny walked inside. Here everything was just as nice as it could be. A bright fire danced in the fireplace and threw long

shadows on the wall. There was a little chair just before it. She ran through the house, looking at everything.

"How happy I am!" sighed Tiny, as she went to bed. "No longer will I have to go about asking for bread. Now I can help poor people. I will bring them here and be good to them."

And so Tiny and the poor people she helped were happy ever after in their pretty little home.

QUESTIONS
---

1. Why was Tiny unhappy at first?
2. What things did Tiny wish for?
3. If you had a "wishing book," what would you wish for?
4. What did Tiny do after she had everything she wanted?
5. How can we help our wishes come true?

Me, Myself, and I

American Folk Rhyme

Me, myself, and I—
We went to the kitchen and ate a pie.
Then my mother, she came in
And chased us out with a rolling pin.

Clouds Tell the Story

Nancy Larrick

Look at the sky above you. Today it is clear blue. Tiny clouds drift across like feathers on parade. Far across the pond, great white clouds are rolling up. They seem to pile on top of each other to make a boiling mountain above the trees.

Farmers are watching those clouds. Air pilots are watching, too. They know that clouds can bring rain, hail, sleet, or snow.

Weather forecasters watch the clouds day and night. To them the clouds tell a story. When clouds are heavy and black, they say, "A storm is coming."

For years men looked at the clouds as ants do—from underneath. No one had seen a cloud from above.

Then the airplane was invented. Men could fly into the clouds. Like birds, they saw fluffy white clouds all around them.

Often they flew over the clouds. As they looked down, they saw a sea of white. Sometimes it looked like a sea of soap-suds. Always floating. Always moving.

From the earth we can see only part of a cloud. We don't know how high it is. We don't know how wide it is. Most important, we can't see all the clouds coming toward us.

From the air we can learn more. So weather stations began sending up airplanes to get reports on the clouds. They sent up balloons, too, to get reports on the clouds.

That was fine in good weather. But in bad weather, airplanes and balloons have trouble. A heavy storm can bring a balloon down. But weather forecasters want to know what happens in a heavy storm. They want a report from above the clouds, even in bad weather.

Today they are getting weather reports from outer space. One of the man-made satellites takes pictures 4,000 miles above the earth. It works like a TV camera taking pictures as it goes around the earth.

Some pictures show an area 800 miles wide and 800 miles long. One picture shows the clouds from New York to Chicago. Then comes a picture of clouds from Chicago to Denver. In a flash, weather forecasters see more clouds than they ever saw before.

*   *   *   *   *   *

On a clear day, find a big open space and look high in the sky. Do you see some clouds that are like thin streaks of curls?

It seems as though an artist's brush has swept across lightly. A touch here and a touch there. Because these clouds are light and curly, they are called *cirrus* clouds. (*Cirrus* means curl or tuft.)

Cirrus clouds are very high in the sky, perhaps four miles

or more. It is so cold up there that cirrus clouds contain tiny ice crystals instead of water droplets.

Often we see cirrus clouds ahead of a storm.

Lower down in the sky, you may see much bigger clouds pushing up. At the top they may look like giant balls of cotton. At the bottom they are flat. All the time they seem to be swelling and boiling up. They may be two or three miles from bottom to top.

These are *cumulus* clouds. On a sunny afternoon, these clouds are likely to be white. The tips may shine in the sunlight. We might call them "fair-weather" clouds.

But sometimes cumulus clouds turn into black storm clouds. Then they reach as high as three or four miles into the sky. Often they bring thunder and lightning as well as rain and hail.

Sometimes the sky seems covered by a gray sheet. You see no blue sky. You see no white clouds. Streaks of gray cover all. It is as though layers of fog had lifted from the earth to the sky.

The gray sheet is really a low cloud. This is called a *stratus* cloud.

As clouds change, the weather is apt to change.

RAIN

Robert Louis Stevenson

The rain is raining all around,
 It falls on field and tree,
It rains on the umbrellas here,
 And on the ships at sea.

122

In the Neighborhood

I. Read and Spell

streets	schools	alleys
yards	firehouse	mail carrier
trees	sidewalks	bus driver
lawns	cars	neighbors
stores	buses	police officer
houses	churches	street lights

II. Read and Answer

1. What kinds of stores are in your neighborhood?

2. Name three things in the neighborhood that you pass every day on the way to school.

3. Why does a neighborhood need these people?

   police officer   mail carrier   fire fighter

III. Write

Write three sentences. Put a word from Part I in each sentence.

Granny and Her Elephant

Jataka Tale

Once upon a time a rich man gave a baby elephant to a woman.

She took the best care of this great baby and soon became very fond of him.

The children in the village called her Granny, and they called the elephant "Granny's Ganesh."

The elephant carried the children on his back all over the village. They shared their goodies with him, and he played with them.

"Please, Ganesh, give us a swing," they said to him almost every day.

"Come on! Who is first?" Ganesh answered. He picked them up with his trunk, swung them high in the air, and then put them down again, carefully.

But Ganesh never did any work.

He ate and slept, played with the children, and visited with Granny.

One day Ganesh wanted Granny to go off to the woods with him.

"I can't go, Ganesh, dear. I have too much work to do."

Then Ganesh looked at her and saw that she was growing old and feeble.

"I am young and strong," he thought. "I'll see if I cannot find some work to do. If I could bring some money home to her, she would not have to work so hard."

So next morning, bright and early, he started down to the river bank.

There he found a man who was in great trouble. There was a long line of wagons so heavily loaded that the oxen could not draw them through the shallow water.

When the man saw Ganesh standing on the bank, he asked, "Who owns this elephant? I want to hire him to help my oxen pull these wagons across the river."

A child standing nearby said, "That is Granny's Ganesh."

"Very well," said the man, "I'll pay two pieces of silver for each wagon this elephant draws across the river."

Ganesh was glad to hear this promise. He went into the river and drew one wagon after another to the other side.

Then he went up to the man for the money.

The man counted out a piece of silver for each wagon.

When Ganesh saw that the man had counted out but one piece of silver for each wagon, instead of two, he would not touch the money at all. He stood in the road and would not let the wagons pass him.

The man tried to get Ganesh out of the way, but not one step would he move.

Then the man went back and counted out another piece of silver for each of the wagons. He put the silver in a bag tied around Ganesh's neck.

Then Ganesh started for home, proud to think that he had a present for Granny.

The children had missed Ganesh and had asked Granny where he was. But she said that she did not know where he had gone.

They looked for him, but it was nearly night before they heard him coming.

"Where have you been, Ganesh? And what is that around your neck?" the children cried, running to meet their playmate.

But Ganesh would not stop to talk with his playmates. He ran straight home to Granny.

"Oh, Ganesh!" she said. "Where have you been? What is in that bag?" And she took the bag off his neck.

Ganesh told her that he had earned some money for her.

"Oh, Ganesh, Ganesh," said Granny, "how hard you must have worked to earn these pieces of silver! What a good Ganesh you are!"

And after that Ganesh did all the hard work, and Granny rested, and they were both very happy.

QUESTIONS

1. Why did Ganesh decide to help Granny?
2. How did he help her?
3. What did Ganesh do when the man did not give him enough money?
4. Why do you like Ganesh?

SIMILES

Anonymous

As wet as a fish—as dry as a bone;

As live as a bird—as dead as a stone;

As plump as a partridge—as poor as a rat;

As slow as a snail—as quick as a cat;

As hard as a flint—as soft as a mole;

As white as a lily—as black as coal;

As plain as a pikestaff—as rough as a bear;

As tight as a drum—as free as the air;

As heavy as lead—as light as a feather;

As steady as time—uncertain as weather;

As hot as a furnace—as cold as a frog;

As gay as a lark—as sick as a dog;

As fierce as a tiger—as mild as a dove;

As stiff as a poker—as limp as a glove;

As blind as a bat—as deaf as a post;

As cool as a cucumber—as warm as toast;

As good as a feast—as bad as a fight;

As light as day—as dark as night.

Selma Burke

If you have a dime in your pocket, take it out and look at it. The man whose head you see on the dime is Franklin D. Roosevelt, our thirty-second president. This head was copied from a statue made by Selma Burke. Selma Burke is a sculptor—someone who models and carves statues.

* * * * * *

Many years ago, when there was time for dreaming, little Selma played on the banks of the river near her home. The summer sun was hot in North Carolina, and the chalky white clay of the river bank was warm and soft to Selma's touch. She liked to squeeze the clay in her hands, shape it, and mark it with a stick.

At last she heard her mother calling. Quickly she put handfuls of clay into the pail she had brought and went up the hill to her house. Her job on this day was to make whitewash for her mother. She would mix the white clay with water until the mixture was thin and smooth, almost like white paint. Then her mother would brush this whitewash on the house and

fence. This was the way the people of that time kept their homes clean and pretty. Making whitewash was the job Selma liked best. It gave her a chance to play with the clay she loved.

Selma was one of ten children. Her father was a minister. Her mother was an office worker who lived to be 103. Selma's family moved all around the country when she was a child. But wherever she went, she felt at home in the warmth of her family circle. And she had her art to keep her happy.

When Selma was a young woman she went to work as a nurse in New York. All the while she studied art and kept on doing sculpture. Later, she also studied art in Paris and other big cities of Europe. She made friends with many other artists, both black and white.

When World War II broke out, Selma joined the Navy. She drove a truck at the Brooklyn Navy Yard. There she hurt her back badly on the job. While she was in the hospital, she entered an art contest. The winner was to make a statue of Franklin D. Roosevelt, who was then president. To her surprise and great joy, she won the contest! She went to see President Roosevelt in the White House. For four hours she made drawings of him on a roll of brown paper. Later she made a statue based on these drawings. And then her statue was copied to make the head on the dime.

Selma Burke is still a sculptor, but she is also a teacher of art. She started a school of art in Pittsburgh and has taught thousands of children during the past 25 years. Although her art can be seen on our money, she says: "I want to show the children that art is not money. . . . It's a life." Perhaps when she looks at the dime she thinks not of what it will buy, but of the child on the river bank with a handful of clay and a dream.

QUESTIONS
---

1. Whose head do you see on a dime?
2. What is a sculptor?
3. How long did Selma's mother live?
4. What did Selma do when World War II broke out?
5. What does Selma Burke do now?
6. How does Selma Burke feel about art?

All Kinds of Things

I. Read and Spell

FAST AND SLOW THINGS

turtle	jet plane	deer
train	snail	spaceship

BIG AND LITTLE THINGS

elephant	seed	sky
flea	world	ant
whale	oak tree	sun
germ	skyscraper	ocean

OLD AND NEW THINGS

moon	mountain	castle
rocket	ocean	television

II. Read and Answer

1. Name some more things that are fast or slow, big or little, old or new.

2. Name some green things, some pretty things, some heavy things, and some light things.

I. A. You have read these stories in the third part of your book. Tell what each one is about.

      Clouds Tell the Story

      The Wishing Book

      Selma Burke

      The Three Bears

      Granny and Her Elephant

  B. Which story did you like best? Why?

  C. Read the story you liked best to your class, or read it again to yourself.

II. A. Learn by heart a poem you read in Part Three of your book, and recite it to your class.

  B. Copy the poem you like best in the third part of your book. Copy it carefully.

Part Four

For Readers
Brave and Bold

The stories that come after this
Are very hard, we're told,
But now we can read anything:
We're readers brave and bold.

The Man, the Boy, and the Donkey

Aesop

One day a man and a boy were leading a donkey to market to sell it. On the way they passed some young men who laughed at them because they were leading the donkey when one of them could be riding it.

When the man heard them laughing, he had his son ride on the donkey, and the man walked beside him. They went along in this way for a while until they met an old man.

"You lazy rascal," the old man called out. "You ought to walk and let your father ride the donkey."

The boy blushed with shame and got off the donkey so that his father could ride it. The father then got on the donkey, and the boy walked beside him. They went along in this way for a little while until they met a young man.

WORDS TO WATCH		
rascal	blushed	decided
ought	shame	frightened

"How selfish that father is—to ride on the donkey while his son walks!" said the young man.

The father then decided that the thing to do was to have his son ride on the donkey with him. So the boy got on the donkey with him, and they rode the donkey for a while until they met an old woman.

"How cruel you are to be both riding on that poor little donkey. You will break its back," said the old woman.

When the boy and his father heard these words, they decided that the only thing to do was to carry the donkey. So they tied its legs together on a long pole and carried it to market.

But when they entered the town, the people laughed at the strange sight. They laughed so loud that the donkey became frightened. While the man and the boy were carrying the donkey over a bridge, the donkey kicked himself free, tumbled into the river, and was drowned.

There was nothing for the man and the boy to do now but to go back home. On their way home, the father said to the boy, "At least we have learned one thing: If you try to please everyone, you please no one, not even yourself."

Blow, Wind, Blow

Mother Goose

Blow, wind, blow! and go, mill, go!
That the miller may grind his corn;
That the baker may take it,
And into rolls make it,
And send us some hot in the morn.

Jane Goodall

A girl was watching a sea gull as it dived toward the water. The gull was looking for food. The girl counted the number of times the gull dived before it found food. She wrote a sentence about the gull in her notebook. Then she started walking home, watching for other birds as she went.

This girl, Jane Goodall, lived in England on the seacoast. She spent most of her time watching birds and animals. She watched robins, starlings, blackbirds, field mice, moles, and rabbits. She wrote notes about the things they did. Jane wanted to learn how these birds and animals behaved. She spent her pocket money on books about animal behavior.

When Jane was eighteen, she left school to work in an office. She wanted to save enough money to go to Africa. After a time, she had enough. She was ready for the trip.

In Africa, she met a famous scientist who was interested in animal behavior. His name was Dr. Louis Leakey. Jane became Dr. Leakey's helper and friend. Dr. Leakey knew that Jane did fine work with animals. He asked her to work on a special project on chimpanzees.

Jane went into the African forest and set up a camp near a large lake. She lived alone at a place where a group of chimpanzees lived. Jane hoped to make friends with the chimpanzees. She wanted to watch them and learn how they behaved.

At first, the chimpanzees ran away before Jane could get close to them. They had never seen a human being before. They were afraid of Jane.

Jane learned where the chimpanzees went to eat in the morning. She would get up early and go there before the chimps did. She sat quietly so that the chimps would learn to know her. Slowly, the chimpanzees lost their fear of Jane.

During her first year in the forest, the chimps stopped running away when they saw Jane. Then they let her come as close as thirty feet. By the end of the second year, they would come to Jane's camp.

Jane started a "Banana Club" for the chimpanzees. When the chimps came to Jane's camp, she gave them bananas. She had names for all the chimps in the club.

Many people wanted to know more about Jane's work. She wrote articles about the chimpanzees and their ways of doing things. A film maker from Holland made a movie about Jane and the chimps. It was shown on television.

If you take a trip to Africa, you might stop at Jane's camp. You would meet Jane and all the members of the Banana Club.

When the chimps knew that Jane was their friend, she

started her real work. She watched them as they played, worked, ate, and raised their young. Jane copied many of their ways. She spent a lot of time in the trees. She ate leaves, bananas, and even insects. She learned things about chimps that no one had known before.

Jane learned that chimps do not eat only leaves and fruit. They hunt for small animals to eat. She was the first to learn that chimpanzees make and use crude tools. Until Jane saw chimpanzees using sticks as tools, scientists had thought that humans were the only living beings to make and use tools. Many scientists say that this discovery is Jane's most important one.

QUESTIONS

1. Why did Jane watch birds and small animals?
2. Where did Jane want to go when she was eighteen?
3. What did Dr. Leakey ask Jane to do?
4. Why did the chimpanzees run away from Jane?
5. How long did it take for the chimps to lose their fear of Jane?
6. What was Jane's real work with the chimpanzees?
7. What did Jane learn about chimpanzees?
8. Is Jane Goodall a brave person? Why?

A Kite

Anonymous

I often sit and wish that I
Could be a kite up in the sky,
And ride upon the breeze and go
Whichever way I chanced to blow.

Scrambled Words

I. Unscramble

tca	okob	likm	iregt
yks	sifh	tals	lebat
rac	enni	ered	engre
ite	ilma	pmal	erapp
pmo	latl	lisk	rbdoa
npe	kesd	alwl	sserd
toh	rkea	tila	moeh

II. Read and Answer

Find two words in each of these scrambled words:

apn   pti   erso   ared   tela

III. Unscramble and Write

1. Fi het act si yaaw, hte cime liwl lapy.

2. Ihts si tno na yeas hgitn ot od.

The Elf and the Dormouse

Oliver Herford

Under a toadstool
　Crept a wee elf,
Out of the rain
　To shelter himself.

Under the toadstool,
　Sound asleep,
Sat a big dormouse
　All in a heap.

Trembled the wee elf,
  Frightened, and yet
Fearing to fly away
  Lest he get wet.

To the next shelter—
  Maybe a mile!
Sudden the wee elf
  Smiled a wee smile.

Tugged till the toadstool
  Toppled in two.
Holding it over him,
  Gaily he flew.

Soon he was safe home,
  Dry as could be.
Soon woke the dormouse—
  "Good gracious me!

Where is my toadstool?"
  Loud he lamented.
And that's how umbrellas
  First were invented.

Dick Whittington and His Cat

English Folk Tale

Dick Whittington was a poor boy who lived in the country. He had no mother or father, and he had no money to buy food. He dreamed about going to London because he had heard that the streets there were paved with gold.

One day a man on a wagon took Dick to London with him.

WORDS TO WATCH		
Whittington	treasure	seized
London	kingdom	amazed
cruel	Barbary	married
mayor	palace	elected

But when Dick got to London, he found no gold streets. He only saw poor and hungry people like himself.

Dick looked for work, and after a time a kind man hired him as a helper to his cook. But the cook was cruel. He beat Dick and made him sleep in an attic full of mice.

One day when Dick had saved a penny, he bought a cat. He named the cat Tabby. Tabby was very good at catching mice, and soon there were no more mice in the attic.

Dick's master owned many ships. One day he called all his servants together. He told them that one of his ships was about to sail to a faraway land. There would be many things on the ship to be traded and sold.

"Each of you may send something of your own on the ship," he said. "When it is sold you may get much gold and silver." Poor Dick had nothing except Tabby, his cat, so he sent that.

After the cat left, Dick became so lonely and unhappy that he decided to run away. He had not gone far when he heard church bells ringing. They said:

Turn around, Dick Whittington, turn round,
Three times Mayor of London Town.

Dick did not know what the bells meant, but he turned around and went back home.

Some weeks later the ship came back. It was filled with sacks of gold and silver and fine things for everyone. But the biggest treasure of all was for Dick.

"How could a little cat be worth so much?" the people asked. Then the captain of the ship told them the story.

He said that in the country of Barbary, the king and queen had invited him to dinner in the palace. But when the food was brought out, mice ran out from all sides. They seized the food and ran away with it.

The king and queen said this happened all the time. They said they would give half their treasure to anyone who would help them get rid of the mice.

Then the captain went off to his ship and brought Tabby back. In a few minutes she had killed all the mice in the room. The king and queen were amazed. They had never seen a cat before, for there were no cats in the Kingdom of Barbary.

They said that such a wonderful animal was well worth half the treasure. And that was how Dick became one of the richest people in London.

Dick went to school, and when he grew up, he married his master's daughter. But Dick never forgot that he had once been poor and hungry, and he was good to the people. That is why he was elected Mayor of London three times.

QUESTIONS

1. Why did Dick Whittington go to London?
2. How was the cook cruel to Dick?
3. What did the master say to the servants?
4. Why did Dick turn back to London?
5. How did Dick Whittington's cat make Dick rich?
6. Do you like Dick? Why?

The Fairies

William Allingham

Up the airy mountain,
    Down the rushy glen,
We daren't go a-hunting
    For fear of little men;
Wee folk, good folk,
    Trooping all together;
Green jacket, red cap,
    And white owl's feather!

Down along the rocky shore
    Some make their home,
They live on crispy pancakes
    Of yellow tide-foam;
Some in the reeds
    Of the black mountain-lake,
With frogs for their watch-dogs,
    All night awake.

Part Five

On Your Own

The Garden

Arnold Lobel

Frog was in his garden.

Toad came walking by.

"What a fine garden

you have, Frog," he said.

"Yes," said Frog. "It is very nice,

but it was hard work."

"I wish I had a garden," said Toad.

"Here are some flower seeds.

Plant them in the ground," said Frog,

"and soon you will have a garden."

"How soon?" asked Toad.

"Quite soon," said Frog.

Toad ran home.

He planted the flower seeds.

"Now seeds," said Toad,

"start growing."

Toad walked up and down

a few times.

The seeds did not start to grow.

Toad put his head

close to the ground

and said loudly,

"Now seeds, start growing!"

Toad looked at the ground again.

The seeds did not start to grow.

Toad put his head
very close to the ground and shouted,
"NOW SEEDS, START GROWING!"
Frog came running up the path.
"What is all this noise?" he asked.
"My seeds will not grow," said Toad.

"You are shouting too much,"
said Frog. "These poor seeds
are afraid to grow."

"My seeds are afraid to grow?"
asked Toad.

"Of course," said Frog.

"Leave them alone for a few days.
Let the sun shine on them,
let the rain fall on them.
Soon your seeds will start to grow."

That night
Toad looked out of his window.

"Drat!" said Toad.

"My seeds have not
started to grow.
They must be afraid of the dark."

Toad went out to his garden
with some candles.

"I will read the seeds a story,"
said Toad.

"Then they will not be afraid."

Toad read a long story
to his seeds.

All the next day
Toad sang songs
to his seeds.

And all the next day
Toad read poems
to his seeds.

And all the next day
Toad played music
for his seeds.
Toad looked at the ground.
The seeds still did not
start to grow.
"What shall I do?" cried Toad.
"These must be
the most frightened seeds
in the whole world!"

Then Toad felt very tired,
and he fell asleep.

"Toad, Toad, wake up," said Frog.

"Look at your garden!"

Toad looked at his garden.

Little green plants were coming up
out of the ground.

"At last," shouted Toad,

"my seeds have stopped
being afraid to grow!"

"And now you will have
a nice garden too," said Frog.

"Yes," said Toad,

"but you were right, Frog.

It was very hard work."

HILL OF FIRE

Thomas P. Lewis

Once there was a farmer who lived in Mexico. He lived in a little village, in a house which had only one room. The farmer was not happy. "Nothing ever happens," he said.

The people in the village thought the farmer was foolish. "We have everything we need," they said. "We have a school, and a market, and a church with an old bell that rings on Sundays. Our village is the best there is."

"But nothing ever happens," said the farmer.

Every morning, when the farmer woke up, the first thing he saw was the roof of his little house. Every morning for breakfast he ate two flat cakes of ground corn. His wife had made them the night before. He put honey over the cakes, and drank cinnamon tea from a clay mug.

"Nothing ever happens," he said.

It was still dark and the farmer got ready to leave for the field. His son Pablo was still asleep.

"Perhaps today," said his wife, "something will happen."

"No," said the farmer. "Nothing will."

The farmer led his ox away and did not look back.

At night the farmer returned. He fed his ox. Then he sat down by the fire.

Pablo played with five smooth stones. He threw the stones at a hole he had dug in the earth. "See, Papa!" said Pablo. "I got one in!"

But the farmer was tired. He did not answer. Every day was the same.

One morning the farmer woke up very early. He pulled on his woolen shirt. He took his big hat from a peg on the wall. "I must go to the field early," he said. "The plowing is not done. Soon it will be time to plant the corn."

All morning the farmer worked in his field. The ox helped him. When there was a big rock in the way, the ox stopped and lay down. The farmer pushed the rock away. *"Tst-tst!"* said the farmer. The ox looked at the farmer. Then the ox got up and pulled again.

Late in the morning, when the sun was high, Pablo came to the field.

"Pablo!" said the farmer. "Why are you not in school?"

"There is no school today, Papa," said Pablo. "I have

come to help you plow." The farmer smiled. He reached into his pocket, and gave the boy a small wooden toy.

"A bull!" cried Pablo. The farmer had made it for his son during the hot time of the day when he rested from his work.

Pablo helped the farmer plow the field. The ox pulled, and the plow turned up the soil. Suddenly the plow stopped. The farmer and his son pushed, and the ox pulled, but the plow did not move. It sank into the earth. It went down, down,

down, into a little hole. The little hole became a bigger hole. There was a noise deep under the ground, as if something big had growled.

The farmer looked. Pablo looked. The ox turned its head. White smoke came from the hole in the ground.

"Run!" said the farmer. "Run!"

There was a loud CRACK, and the earth opened wide. The farmer ran, Pablo ran, and the ox ran too. Fire and smoke came from the ground.

The farmer ran all the way to the village. He ran inside the church and rang the old bell.

The other farmers came from their fields. People came out of their houses. "Look!" said the farmer. "Look there!"

That night no one slept. Everyone watched the fire in the sky. It came from where the farmer's field had been. There was a loud BOOM, and another, and another. Hot lava came out of the earth. Steaming lava spread over the ground, through the trees. It came toward the farmer's house. It came toward the village. Pieces of burning stone flew in the air. The earth was coughing. Every time it coughed, the hill of fire grew bigger.

In a few days the hill was as big as a mountain. And every few minutes there was a loud BOOM. Squirrels and rabbits

ran, and birds flew away from the fire. People led their burros and their oxen to safety. Pieces of burning ash flew everywhere. The farmer and his neighbors put wet cloths over their noses to keep out the smoke.

Some of the people went close to the steaming lava. They carried big crosses. They prayed for the fire to stop. The farmer and Pablo watched from the side of a hill.

When the booming stopped and the fires grew smaller, the farmer's house was gone. The school was gone. The market was gone. Half the village was gone.

One day some men in uniform came in cars and trucks.

"So you are the one with the plow that opened up the

earth," they said to the farmer. They laughed. "You are lucky to be alive, *amigo*."

The soldiers looked at the village. "Everyone must go!" the captain said. "It is not safe to live here any longer."

The farmer and his wife and Pablo and all the people of the village went with the soldiers. They rode away in the trucks.

The farmer found a new house. It was bigger than the one they lived in before. It was not far from the old one. But it was far enough away to be safe from *El Monstruo,* which means "The Monster." That is the name the people gave to the great volcano.

The people made a new village. They made a new school and a new market. They had a great *fiesta* because now they were safe. At the *fiesta* the band played, and the people danced and clapped their hands.

People from the city came in a bus to see *El Monstruo*. The people of the village sold them oranges and melons and hot dogs and corn cakes to eat.

Now the farmer had a new field. Every morning he woke up early. It was still dark, and *El Monstruo* glowed in the sky. Every morning for breakfast he ate two flat cakes of ground corn. His wife had made them the night before. The farmer went to his new field. His ox went with him, just as before.

Sometimes Pablo brought the children of the village to see the farmer. From the field they could see the volcano smoking, like an old man smoking his pipe. "Can you make another hill of fire?" the children said.

"No, my friends, no, no," said the farmer. He laughed. "One hill of fire is enough for me."

Do You Ever Wonder?

David E. Fisher

Albert Einstein was a young boy in school when he first thought of a little question. In fact, he thought about that question so much in school that his teachers became angry. Whenever the rest of the class was studying or singing or learning, Albert was staring out the window, paying no attention to his teacher, daydreaming.

"Albert! What are you doing now?"

"I was looking at the sunlight. I was wondering, what if I could ride along on that sunbeam, go just as fast as it is going—"

"Albert! Such nonsense! You must learn to concentrate on your lessons!"

But he never did. As he grew up, as he passed through his teenage years and into adulthood, he kept thinking and wondering about that question.

Do you ever wonder?

About what?

About *everything*. Do you ever wonder about the world and the sky and the stars? About why people can't fly and why the sun doesn't fall on our heads? Do you ever wonder about *light*? About where it comes from when you turn on the switch and where it goes when you turn the switch off?

Most people don't wonder. They have learned that the sun doesn't fall down, and that's enough for them. They don't care about *why*. They know that when they turn on the switch, light will come. They don't care about where it comes from. They know that when they turn off the switch, the light will go away. They don't care where it goes.

But some people do. Some people care, some people wonder. These people are the scientists. They want to understand the world and the universe. They want to know *why* things happen the way they do.

Some scientists wonder mostly about *life*. They are called *biologists*.

Others wonder about the *substances* all around us, things like water and air and clothing and automobile tires. They are called *chemists*.

Others wonder more about *energy*, about light and gravity and motion. They are called *physicists*.

This story is about the greatest physicist of the twentieth century. Some people say he may be the greatest of all time. He spent his life wondering and thinking about the simplest question he could think of. But he wasn't satisfied with a simple answer.

His name was Albert Einstein, and that question was:

What is light?

It's a very little question, but no one could tell him the answer. At least, no one could tell him a *good* answer. No one seemed to know, even though light is the most common thing we have around us. It would be very hard to imagine living without light. Yet no one seemed to know what it is. No one could answer his question.

They told him that it was a silly question. They said that light is just light, and what's all the fuss about?

That didn't seem to Einstein to be a good answer. He didn't believe it was a silly question at all. So he stopped asking about light but he didn't stop thinking about it.

And that was his first discovery. You don't *have* to believe what people tell you. You can *think* about things as much as you like.

So he kept on thinking about it, and the more he thought about it the more he decided that the problem was that light moves so *fast*. When you turn on the light in the kitchen, it fills the whole room *immediately*. And when you turn the light off, it *disappears* immediately.

That must be why we can't see what light really *is*, he thought. It just moves too fast to be seen.

For example, if someone throws a stone and it zips right by your head, you can hardly see it because it's moving so fast. When the stone is stopped, when it's lying on the ground, you can see it clearly.

So Einstein thought it must be the same problem with light. If you could *stop* it, then you could see what it really is. But can you stop light? Can you hold it still?

If you're not sure, try an *experiment*. An experiment is a test to see what will happen. That's what scientists do. Hold a paper bag open and shine some light into it. Then, while the light is still shining, close the bag tight and trap the light in it. Take the bag into a dark room so you can see the light easily. Open the bag and look in. What will you see?

Nothing. The light has disappeared. We *can't* hold it still. But if we can't hold it still, how can we tell what it looks like?

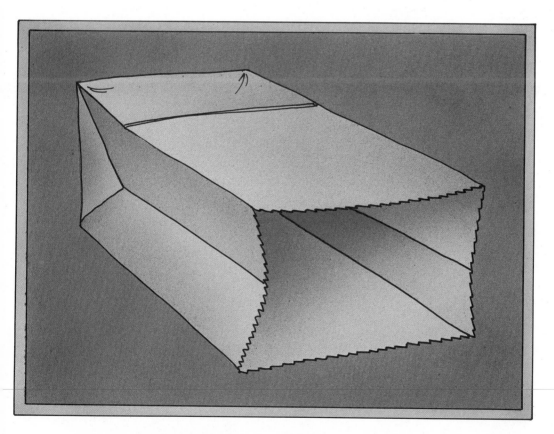

Well, have you ever flown in an airplane? Jet airliners fly at about 600 miles per hour. That's fast! It's certainly faster than the stone whizzing by your head. But if you are inside the airliner, you can see it as clearly as if it weren't moving at all. That's because you are *moving with it*, moving just as fast.

So Einstein thought that it wouldn't matter that light can't be stopped, if he could only move along with it. If he could do that, he would be able to see it as clearly as a person flying inside an airliner can see the airliner. If he could only do that, what would the light look like?

Einstein thought about this question for a long time. So did many other scientists. Finally Einstein decided that it was impossible to answer the question.

But in thinking about light, he found the answers to many other important questions. He discovered what energy is. He learned more about time. His ideas help us understand more about things that happen to us every day. They help us understand things like how gravity works, what an atom is, and what stars are like.

Go, little book, and tell the world

That you have been my friend;

I've turned your pages: one, two, three—

And now I've reached the end.

Glossary

a_, ă_	apple, tan		**ea**	eat, leap, tea
ā	acorn, table		**_ĕa_**	head, bread
à	alone, Donna		**ee**	eel, feet, see
â	air, care		**er**	herd, her
ä	father, wand		**_ew**	few, blew
ạ	all, ball		**f**	far, taffy, off
a_e	ape, bake		**g**	gas, wiggle, sag
ai_	aim, sail		**ġ**	gem, giant, gym
àr	calendar		**gh_**	ghost
är	art, park, car		**_gh**	though, thought (silent)
au_	author, Paul		**h_**	hat
aw	awful, lawn, saw		**i_, ĭ_**	it, sit
_ay	say, day		**ī**	pilot, pie
b	bat, able, tub		**_ï_**	babies, machine, *also*
c	cat, cot, cut			onion, savior, familiar
ce	cent, ace		**i_e**	ice, bite
ch	chest, church		**_igh**	high, bright
c̄h	chorus, ache		**ir**	irk, bird, fir
c̦h	chute		**j_**	jam
ci	cider, decide		**k**	kite, ankle, ink
_ci_	special		**kn_**	knife
_ck	tack, sick		**l**	lamp, wallet, tail
cy	bicycle		**_le**	table, ample
d	dad		**m**	man, bump, ham
_dge	edge, judge		**_mb**	lamb, comb
e_, ĕ_	elf, hen		**n**	no, tent, sun
ē	equal, me		**_ñ_**	uncle, anger
ė	moment, loaded		**_ng**	sing, ring

1. If a word ends in a silent *e,* as in **face,** the silent *e* is not marked. If a word ends in *-ed* pronounced **t,** as in **baked,** or **d,** as in **stayed,** no mark is needed. If the ending *-ed* forms a separate syllable pronounced **ėd,** as in **load'ėd,** the *e* has a dot.

2. If there are two or three vowels in the same syllable and only one is marked, as in **beaū'ty, frĭend, rōgue,** or **breāk,** all the other vowels in the syllable are silent.

o_, ŏ_	odd, pot		_ti_	nation, station, *also* question
ō	go, no, toe			
ȯ	come, wagon		ṭu	congratulate
ô	off, song		u_, ŭ_	up, bus
oa_	oat, soap		ū	use, cute, *also* granulate
o_e	ode, bone			
oi_	oil, boil		ṳ	truth, true
o͝o	book, nook		u̇	nature
o͞o	boot, zoo		ṵ	pull, full
or	order, normal		ur	urge, turn, fur
ȯr	motor, doctor		ūr	cure, pure
ou_	out, hound		v	voice, save
ow	owl, town, cow		w_	will, wash
_ōw	low, throw		wh_	white, what
_oy	boy, toy		wr_	write
p	paper, tap		_x	extra, ax
ph	phone, elephant, graph		_x_	exist, example
qu_	quick, queen		y_	yes, yet
r	ram, born, ear		_y	baby, happy (when it is the only vowel in a final unstressed syllable)
s	sun, ask, yes			
_s̠	toes, hose			
_s̠_	vision, confusion			
ss̠	fission			
sh	show, bishop, fish		_y̆_	cymbal
t	tall, sets, bit		_ȳ	cry, sky
th	thick, three		ẏ	zephyr, martyr
th	this, feather, bathe		z	zoo, nozzle, buzz
_tch	itch, patch			

3. The Open Court diacritical marks in the Pronunciation Key make it possible to indicate the pronunciation of most unfamiliar words without respelling.

ac′ci·dent *n.* An unexpected happening.

ā′corn *n.* The nut of an oak tree.

ad·mire′ *v.* To be pleased with; to look at with approval.

again (a·gen′) *adv.* Once more; another time.

a·lông′side′ *adv.* Beside; next to.

a·maze′ *v.* To surprise; to astonish.

an′i·mal *n.* A living creature that can feel and move.

a·rith′me·tic *n.* The easiest part of mathematics, including addition, subtraction, multiplication, and division.

a·wāk′en *v.* To rouse from sleep.

bam·boo′ *n.* Giant, woodlike grass whose stems are used to make fishing poles and furniture.

Bär′ba·ry *n.* The northern coast of Africa.

bärn′yärd *n.* The land or yard around a barn.

bēast *n.* A four-footed animal.

be·came′ *v.* To have come to be.

be·cause′ *conj.* For the reason that; since.

be·hāv′ior *n.* The way a person or an animal acts.

big′ger *adj.* Larger.

bless′ing *n.* A wish for success or happiness; a person or thing that brings happiness.

blush *v.* To flush; to grow rosy faced.

bored *adj.* Weary; restless; tired.

both′er *v.* To disturb; to annoy.

bough *n.* A branch or limb of a tree.

bôught *v.* To have purchased.

bound *v.* To leap; to hop.

brĕak′fast *n.* The first meal of the day.

Brŏŏk′lyn Nā′vy Yärd *n.* A government dockyard in Brooklyn, New York, where ships are built, repaired, and fitted out.

broth′er *n.* A boy or man who has the same parents as another person.

brôught *v.* To have carried along.

build *v.* To join materials together to make something.

busy (bis′y) *adj.* Fully occupied; active.

butch′er *n.* A person who kills animals and prepares the meat to be sold; a person who sells meat.

cel′lar *n.* An underground room; a basement.

chalky (chak′y) *adj.* Resembling soft, white limestone.

chil′dren *n.* Young people; infants.

chim′nēy *n.* A tubelike passage to carry smoke away.

chim·pan·zee′ *n.* An ape of Africa, with black hair and large ears, noted for its intelligence.

Chī·nese′ *n.* The people of China or their descendants. —*adj.* Of China, its people, language, or culture.

chip′munk *n.* A small, striped ground squirrel.

cir′rus *adj.* Of a kind of cloud that is high in the sky and has narrow, white bands.

clos′er *adj.* Nearer.

clōthes (*or* **clōs**) *n.* Garments; dress; what a person wears.

cob′bler *n.* One who makes and repairs shoes.

côf′fin *n.* A box into which a dead person or animal is put.

could (cŏŏd) *v.* To have been able.

crā′dle *n.* A rocking bed for a baby.

creak *v.* To make a sharp, harsh, squeaking sound.

crū′èl *adj.* Wicked; hurtful; mean.

crum′ple *v.* To wrinkle; to push together.

crȳs′tàl *n.* A body that has angles and flat surfaces, formed when certain substances become solids.

cumulus (cū′myŭ·lus) *adj.* Of a kind of cloud that is white and woolly.

cupboard (cub′èrd) *n.* A cabinet with shelves on which dishes or food is kept.

dè·cide′ *v.* To make up one's mind; to choose.

dè·light′ *n.* Joy; great pleasure; gladness.

dòne *adj.* Finished; completed.

dor′mouse *n.* A small, furry rodent of Europe, similar to a squirrel.

dòve *n.* A bird of the pigeon family.

down′stâirs′ *n.* The stories in a building below the floor where one is.

drop′lèt *n.* A tiny ball-shaped quantity of liquid.

èar′ly *adv.* Beforehand; before the usual or expected time.

edge *n.* A place where something ends.

è·lect′ *v.* To choose by voting.

el′è·phànt *n.* The largest living land animal.

en′ğine *n.* The machine that pulls a train.

enough (è·nòuf′) *adj.* In the amount or number needed; sufficient.

en′vè·lope *n.* A wrapper made of paper, usually for mailing letters.

ev′er·green *n.* A plant or tree that has green leaves all year long.

everyone (ĕve′ry·wun) *pron.* All the people.

fär′ther *adv.* To or at a more advanced point or distance.

fīeld *n.* A large enclosed piece of land.

fifth *adj.* After four others in a series.

fī′nàl·ly *adv.* In the end; at last.

first *adj.* In front of all the others; the foremost or earliest.

flint *n.* A very hard stone that produces sparks when struck against steel.

Pronunciation Key

VOWELS: sat, hăve, āble, fäther, àll, câre, àlone; yet, brĕad, mē, loadèd; it, practĭce, pīlot, machïne; hot, nō, ôff, wagòn; fŏŏt, fōōd; oil, toy; count, town; up, ŭse, trŭth, p̣ull; mȳth, baby, crȳ, zephẏr.
CONSONANTS: cent, cider, cycle; c̄horus, c̣hute; ġem; light and though (silent), ghost; iñk; elephant; toeṣ; ṯhem; speçial, meaṣure, naṯion, naṯure.
SEE THE FULL KEY ON PAGE 186.

flour *n.* Wheat that has been ground into powder for use in baking.

fore′cast·er *n.* A person who tells in advance what the weather will be.

for·lorn′ *adj.* Sad; miserable.

fōur *adj.* Being one more than three; being one less than five.

fōurth *adj.* After three others in a series.

fright′ėned *adj.* Afraid; scared; alarmed.

frūit′er·er *n.* One who sells fruit.

Gȧ′nesh *n.* An Indian name, actually the name of the elephant-headed god of wisdom, patron of students, and son of the god Shiva.

ġer′mi·nate *v.* To sprout; to begin to grow.

ġi·raffe′ *n.* A tall, long-necked, spotted African animal.

gnaw (naw) *v.* To chew; to bite.

gob′lin *n.* A mischievous elf that plays tricks on people and frightens them.

Gōld′ï·locks *n.* A character in the story ''Goldilocks and the Three Bears.''

gŏod′nėss *interj.* An exclamation of surprise or wonder.

groan *v.* To make a low, sad sound; to moan.

growl *v.* To snarl; to make a low warning sound.

hap′pï·er *adj.* More joyful; more contented.

härd′ly *adv.* Barely; scarcely.

hatch′way *n.* An opening of a trap door, as in the ceiling of a cellar.

hat′ter *n.* One who makes or sells hats.

him·self′ *pron.* A word sometimes used instead of *he*.

hoarse *adj.* Harsh-voiced; husky-voiced.

hour (our) *n.* Sixty minutes.

hū′mȧn bē′ing *n.* A creature of the human race; a person.

hum′ming·bird′ *n.* A small, brightly colored bird with a long beak and wings that make a humming noise when it flies.

hun′drėd *adj.* Being one more than ninety-nine.

in·deed′ *adv.* Really; truly.

in·stĕad′ *adv.* In place of.

join′er *n.* A woodworker; a carpenter.

king′dȯm *n.* The land ruled by a king.

knock *v.* To rap on; to strike.

knōw *v.* To be sure; to be certain.

laugh (laf) *v.* To show amusement with the mouth and voice.

lėarn *v.* To gain new knowledge or skill.

limp *adj.* Not stiff; easily twisted or bent.

lodge′pole *adj.* Of a kind of pine tree found in the western United States.

Lon'don *n.* The capital of England.

lot *n.* An undeveloped piece of land.

loud'ly *adv.* In a noisy way.

mag'pie *n.* A noisy black-and-white bird of the crow family.

maid'en *n.* A young unmarried woman.

malt *n.* Barley grain that has begun to sprout and grow.

mär'ket *n.* A place where one goes to buy or sell things.

mar'ry *v.* To wed; to become husband and wife.

may'or *n.* The person in charge of a city government.

mead'ow *n.* A piece of open land covered with grass.

mer'ri·ly *adv.* Happily; joyfully.

mock *v.* To make fun of.

mole *n.* A small, furry animal that lives underground.

moss *n.* A tiny plant growing in moist soil or on rocks and trees close to water.

mouse *n.* A small rodent that usually lives in fields.

Mr. (mis'ter) A title used in speaking of or to a man, placed before the name.

Mrs. (mis'es) A title used in speaking of or to a woman, placed before the name.

nec'tar *n.* The sweet liquid found in flowers.

nee'dle *n.* A long, pointed instrument used in sewing and knitting.

neigh (nā) *n.* A whinny; the sound a horse makes.

news'pa·per *n.* Printed sheets containing news and other items.

once (wunce) *adv.* At one time; on one occasion.

ought *v.* To be right to; should.

our·selves' *pron.* A word used at certain times instead of *us*.

ov'en *n.* An enclosed space for baking, heating, or drying.

pack'et *n.* A small package.

pal'ace *n.* A large, magnificent house, often the official home of a king or ruler.

Pronunciation Key

VOWELS: sat, hăve, āble, fäther, all, câre, alone; yet, brĕad, mē, loadĕd; it, practĭce, pīlot, machïne; hot, nō, ôff, wagon; fŏŏt, fōōd; oil, toy; count, town; up, ūse, trŭth, pull; mўth, baby, crÿ, zephўr.

CONSONANTS: cent, cider, cycle; c̄horus, c̨hute; g̣em; light and though (silent), ghost; iñk; elephant; toes̱; t̲hem; speçial, meaṣure, nat̲ion, nat̨ure.

SEE THE FULL KEY ON PAGE 186.

pär′tridge *n*. A wild bird related to the chicken.

per·haps′ *adv*. Maybe; possibly.

pi′ġeon *n*. A bird that coos, often found in cities.

piñon (pin′yȯn) *adj*. Of a kind of pine tree bearing large seeds that can be eaten.

Pittsburgh (pits′burg) *n*. A large industrial city in Pennsylvania.

plēase *v*. To satisfy; to delight.

plen′ti·ful *adj*. In a large amount; more than enough.

plump *adj*. Chubby; fat.

pō′ker *n*. A rod or bar for stirring logs in a fire.

pȯ·lite′ly *adv*. With good manners.

por′ridge *n*. A cereal cooked in water or milk.

pȯ·tā′tō *n*. A starchy vegetable.

prom′ĭse *n*. A special agreement to do something.

pros′per·ȯus *adj*. Having success, wealth, or good fortune.

quench *v*. To put out.

quī′ĕt *adj*. Noiseless; silent.

rain′storm *n*. A storm with a heavy rain.

ras′cȧl *n*. A mischievous child; a scamp.

reed *n*. A tall water plant.

rė·main′ *v*. To stay.

rė·mem′ber *v*. To recall a past event; to think of again.

rė·plȳ′ *v*. To answer.

rich′er *adj*. More wealthy.

rī′pėn *v*. To become mature and ready to be harvested.

Rōo′sė·velt, Frank′lin D. *n*. The thirty-second president of the United States.

rush *n*. A long-stemmed water plant whose stems are used for making baskets and chair seats.

sat′ėl·lite *n*. A body that revolves around a larger body.

sau′cer *n*. A dish to put a cup on.

sċhōol *n*. A place of instruction and learning.

scī′ėn·tist *n*. A person who studies nature and natural laws.

scōld *n*. A bawling out.

scour *v*. To clean by scrubbing; to brighten.

sculp′tȯr *n*. A person who models and carves statues.

sec′ȯnd *adj*. The next one after the first.

sēize *v*. To grab; to take.

shame *n*. A feeling of disgrace and guilt.

shoe (shūͤe) *n*. A covering for the foot below the ankle.

should (shŏŏd) *v*. Ought to; would.

side′track *n*. A track alongside the main track.

sigh *v*. To say longingly; to let out a loud breath.

sim′i·lē *n*. A comparison that uses the word *like* or *as*.

192

sis′ter *n.* A girl or woman who has the same parents as another person.

snug′gle *v.* To move close to; to nestle.

squâre *n.* A four-sided open area with buildings around it.

squeak *v.* To make a shrill, sharp sound; to squeal.

squir′rel *n.* A small, furry animal with a bushy tail.

staff *n.* A stick; a cane.

sta′tūe *n.* A figure of a person or animal.

strā′tus *adj.* Of a kind of cloud that is low in the sky and looks like a gray sheet.

strōll *v.* To walk slowly; to saunter.

stȳ *n.* A place where pigs are kept.

swäl′lōw *n.* A small, swift bird.

tai′lŏr *n.* One who makes, repairs, or alters clothes.

tat′tered *adj.* Ragged.

tel′e·vĭ·șion *n.* A machine that receives pictures and sounds sent through the air.

third *adj.* After two others in a series.

thôught *v.* To have reasoned; to have formed an opinion or idea.

throūgh *adv.* From one end or side to the other.

tight *adj.* Closely and securely put together.

tī′nĭ·ėst *adj.* Smallest.

tȯ·geth′er *adv.* In a group; in company.

tȯ·mā′tō *n.* A pulpy, red fruit that can be eaten.

tȯ·mor′rōw *n.* The day after today.

trĕaș′ŭre *n.* Riches; valuables.

tripe *n.* The part of the stomach of an ox or cow that is used for food.

trōll *n.* An ugly, bad-tempered imaginary creature.

trôu′ble *n.* Distress; disaster.

twig *n.* A very small branch of a tree.

two (tōo) *adj.* Being one more than one; being one less than three.

un·der·neath′ *adv.* Below; at a lower level.

un·der·stŏŏd′ *v.* To have come to know.

un·hap′py *adj.* Sad; miserable.

Pronunciation Key

VOWELS: sat, hăve, āble, fäther, ạll, câre, ȧlone; yet, brĕad, mē, loadėd; it, practĭce, pīlot, machïne; hot, nō, ôff, wagȯn; fŏŏt, fōōd; oil, toy; count, town; up, ūse, trŭth, pụll; mȳth, baby, crȳ, zephẏr.
CONSONANTS: **c**ent, **c**ider, **c**ycle; **c̄**horus, **c̣**hute; **ġ**em; light and though (silent), **gh**ost; i**ñ**k; **el**ephant; toe**ş**; **th**em; spe**ç**ial, mea**ş**ure, na**t**ion, na**t̠**ure.
SEE THE FULL KEY ON PAGE 186.

193

un·kīnd′ *adj*. Mean; cruel.

up′stâirs̲′ *n*. The stories in a building above the floor where one is.

vā′cȧnt *adj*. Empty; not occupied.

wheat *n*. A type of tall grain that farmers grow for its seeds; also, the seeds themselves.

white′wäsh *n*. A mixture of lime and water, used to make walls white.

Whit′ting·tȯn, Rich′ȧrd *n*. A mayor of London long ago.

wig′gly *adj*. Twisting; moving from side to side with short, quick movements.

wȯr′ry *v*. To pester; to tease.

wȯrse *adj*. More unpleasant, disagreeable, or harmful.

yȯung′ėst *adj*. Last born; least old.